RADICAL GRACE

RADICAL GRACE

ESSAYS AND CONVERSATIONS ON TEACHING

by

Candice Price & Miloš Savić

619 Wreath

First edition, 2022

ISBN 978-1-958469-01-9

Published by 619 Wreath

ACKNOWLEDGMENTS

LAND ACKNOWLEDGEMENT:

Candice: As a descendant of enslaved Africans, I take a step toward honoring the truth and achieving healing and reconciliation with an acknowledgment that my home was built upon and within the ancestral homelands of the Nonotuck Peoples (Pocumtuck). Thus, I acknowledge the privilege I had to work on this project on land that was violently stolen. My present-day neighboring Indigenous nations include the Nipmuc and the Wampanoag to the East, the Mohegan and Pequot to the South, the Mohican to the West, and the Abenaki to the North. I practice this acknowledgment to recognize and respect the Indigenous Peoples as traditional stewards and owners of this land. They existed before the violence of colonization and are still here. Indigenous peoples continue to experience forced removal, genocide, theft of their ancestral lands, and other atrocities connected to colonization. This acknowledgment is just one action I can take to correct the stories and practices that erase Indigenous people's history and culture. It is a step towards being a more equitable and inclusive nation.

Miloš: It is my responsibility to recognize and acknowledge the people, culture and history that make up our entire community here in Oklahoma. This land that I am on was the traditional home of the Kickapoo, Osage, Kiowa, Wichita, & Quapaw tribes. The state of Oklahoma has 39 tribal nations as a result of settler and colonial policies that were designed to assimilate Native people. I want to recognize the sovereign rights of all 39 of Oklahoma's Indigenous tribes, as well as the rights of all tribes in the world. It is their land. Although a first step, I also want to advocate for putting more than an acknowledgment. I must act more in my capacity, whether it is to donate, volunteer, or support their nations to create a more equitable future.

ACKNOWLEDGEMENTS:

We want to acknowledge those that fuel us every day: Jean Tashima for the cover art, logo, and creativity; Casey Haskins, who took a rough draft and made it incredible; and the Board for their love and unyielding support.

Finally, we are donating a portion of the profits from this book to the Native Forward Scholars Fund. You can find out more information about the fund on our website 619wreath.com.

DEDICATION

"Wisdom is like fire. People take it from others."

–Anonymous

THIS IS DEDICATED TO OUR students, families, and friends that show us radical grace everyday. We love you.

TO OUR FANS: thank you for picking up this book. May you find something in this book you never considered before.

PREFACE

If you are ever scared you're a bad person, remember that bad people don't care about being better.

–Anonymous

IN 2019, WE STARTED TALKING ABOUT TEACHING. The more we shared and discussed, the more we thought about our viewpoint around teaching. We weren't able to name it, but we knew it was something. Then I, Candice, shared my thoughts on teaching with Amanda Ruiz, a good friend and also professor of mathematics. Amanda looked thoughtfully and said "It is *Radical Grace*. The way you think about teaching is based on radical grace." And this is how it started. We began recording our weekly talks in hopes of creating a podcast, and landed on compiling those conversations and thoughts into a book. Some ideas and thoughts overlap often in these conversations. So while we tried to edit as best we could, we also wanted to keep the flow of the conversation genuine. Thus, you will see some concepts and metaphors repeated in various chapters and over various discussions.

It is also important that we acknowledge all of the aspects of our lives that have guided us towards radical grace: the many conversations about teaching that we've had with others, reflecting on our own triumphs and mistakes, and seeking resources in the form of books, articles, podcasts, videos, and speakers at conferences. These experiences have shaped us and our conversations in many ways. There are too many people to name but please know that we thank you all for your candid discussions and support. So... here we are.

Candice: So, we have been discussing the holistic reason why we do what we do, and I mentioned to you that I wouldn't teach this way if I wasn't a Black woman in mathematics. Because I believe that my experiences have really shaped how I think about my interactions with students, and I think about how my presence in the classroom is seen and how it is represented.

So I... I know that, while this method of thoughtful teaching, which might be a little rude to say it that way, but this method of thinking about how I teach, people will feel maybe a certain way about it. A common question may sound like: "Why do I have to do all these things when

How can I adapt and change what I'm doing in order to reflect what I think will support the students even more?

what I'm doing works for me? I don't need to change it." But for me, I've been consistently reflecting on my teaching because I can see that some methods didn't work for me as a student. So why would I assume the same methods will work for my students, right?! And how can I adapt and change what I'm doing in order to reflect what I think will support the students even more?

Miloš: If you see statistical trends in mathematics, especially at the PhD level, there seems to be methods that aren't working. For many groups. And that has always caused me to reflect.

I think the other thing you bring up, like: What if I didn't get kicked out of school? I don't know if I would have even embraced or thought about active learning or grace in any measure in the classroom. But I was provided grace, weirdly enough, and I saw the effects. This experience, even just in one class, the only class that I had that was active learning in grad school, it opened everything in my mind. And so, the experiences we experienced have probably brought us to this point. As far as for others who may not appreciate our conversations, you know, a philosopher once said: "the haters are going to hate."

C: "Players are going to play". Is that the same philosopher?

M: That's correct, yes.

Radical Grace

Grace sometimes looks like transparency.
Grace sometimes looks like forgiveness.
Grace sometimes looks like trust.
Grace sometimes looks like support.
Grace should never be forced.
Grace should never be something that has to be earned.
We are deserving of grace from others, for others, for ourselves.
This is Radical Grace.

Contents

Acknowledgments   iii

Dedication   v

Preface   vi

How did We get here?   1

What is Radical Grace?   8

What about Equality and Equity?   17

What does Radical Grace look like in the Classroom?   21

How do we show Radical Grace to Ourselves and Others?   29

Teaching to Swim   36

How would you Describe the "Little Grace"?   39

What if They take Advantage?   51

Access to Rest   59

What is the Formula for Radical Grace?   62

Does Balance imply Change?   68

Puzzles   78

Is there Scarcity in Grace?   82

What is the Lasting Impact of Radical Grace?   94

What does Radical Grace look like in the Future?   110

Appendix A: RAMP UP Seminar   130

Appendix B: References, Resources, and Inspiration   153

Chapter I

How did We get here?

The experiences we have, the places and people we interact with, they change us. It might be small, it might be ginormous, but it is, and always will be, a change. This conversation centered around the stories that made a difference in each of us finding and fostering our own radical grace.

M: I was being interviewed for this temporary teaching job, like an emergency hire for teaching. And I was 23 at the time. I came in there and they asked me a series of questions for a psychological exam. One of them was like, "What will you do if a person cheats on an exam in your class?" And I was like, "I will take them straight to the principal. I will, you know, punish them as much as possible, to the fullest extent of the rules of the school. The fullest extent."

At the end of the range of questions and scenarios, the person who is interviewing me said, "You barely passed the psychological test." I was like, "what?" I didn't understand at all. And he said, "You have zero empathy, whatsoever. You don't even think about what a student is going through whether it be at their home or school life. Have you thought about why they would cheat in your class?" I remember this quote was one of the first eye openers for me in my life.

Where was my radical grace?

In some respects, it was my radical *anti-grace* that was present. In retrospect, that response showed a lot about me: both my privilege in growing up and my pedagogical beliefs. Why would I ever consider the reasons for cheating, when cheating equals "bad"? It was clear cut, and it's the first instance where nuance entered teaching in my mind.

C: I mean, I think that's how we're sort of trained. Like, I remember some of the training at the beginning of my teaching career was like, "be really hard at first and then ease up, but don't let them see you sweat. And make sure they know you're in charge, and you know you can't give them any breaks because they'll take advantage of you, especially as a woman, especially as a woman of color." So you're always worried that someone is trying to get over on you. It's tiring. It's so tiring to think that way about your students, where you can't trust them. And not only that, you start to create assessments that are like "gotcha" assessments. Or you grade harshly when they're close and they understand the material, but it's just like a small mistake. It became an adversarial relationship and that's not fun for anyone. It's not fun for anyone. I don't want to be in a battle with my students while they're learning...I want to be in a partnership.

> *I don't want to be in a battle with my students while they're learning... I want to be in a partnership.*

And so, at first, my philosophy was this idea of, you know, you have to be really rough at the beginning. I have to be very strict and stringent with things like how I graded, deadlines, and all this stuff. Now, I like to teach with a lot of grace.

I read this paper or article by Francis Su, "The Lesson of Grace in Teaching", and I read that actually a few years into my teaching career. And it was exactly what I had needed as a student, because I struggled in my math classes, and not just mathematically. I won't say I *didn't* struggle mathematically because math is hard. But I also struggled with just finding my space, finding my place in the classroom and feeling comfortable being wrong, feeling comfortable asking for support, and not feeling judged. And I didn't always get that. I had many teachers who just ignored me, and never even checked in with me, and I was struggling with the class, with my personal life, everything. And so I think about that impact it had on me. Who even knows the kinds of things I could have done if someone had just reached out and said, "Are you okay? You know we care about you. What can I do to help?"

There were classes I failed. And no one even asked me, no one even cared. And so I think we do a huge disservice to our students when we act like the relationship we have with them is just within the classroom space, and it is only adversarial. It's us against them. And they can tell that. It takes a long time for a student to feel comfortable and to build trust... and some of them never will. And this is because of things that have happened to them. But, then it is now not for us to then judge them and be like "well if you don't trust me, I don't trust you."

We have to give them that grace.

M: So you mentioned that part of your influence on your teaching philosophy is what you experienced. Have there also been influences after that experience that have shaped you?

C: Oh, totally. So I think that there will still be a lot of residual impacts from my original teaching philosophy, even when I thought I was being very graceful and sort of liberal with how I thought about my students. I used to - well not used to, I think I still do it whenever I can - do weekly reflection journals with my students. The first time that I did it, it wasn't a weekly thing, but it was an end-of-the-year sort of thing where they wrote a letter to their beginning of the semester self, from their end of the semester self about the semester. The letter would express an answer to the prompt: What have you learned, not just inside the classroom but outside of the classroom? What are some things you would tell yourself on day one of this class?

In that class, I had a student who kind of disappeared at one point in the semester. And this student was a white man who was a non-traditional student. In my previous experience with math, with teaching, and learning how to teach people, I was told "Well, there are just going to be people who don't respect you as a Black woman in the classroom and won't treat you well." And so, for some reason, I assumed that that's what was happening with a student. He just didn't care to learn from me. So the student came back eventually rather late into the semester. And I just thought "Well, good luck", you know? I never reached out to him. I never even sought him out to see what kind of support he needed or anything like that before or after his return. I just *assumed* he knew what support there was and if he wasn't going to ask for it, then he didn't want it, especially from me.

So, I have them write this last journal, this last sort of reflection, and I read his, and I immediately realized my error. So, in this student's reflection, they mentioned that they would have told themselves they were going to lose their support animal. This animal that, you know, gave them this sort of love and emotional support that they didn't have anywhere else. And that he would fall into a very deep depression because of it, and it would take him a while to pull himself out of it. He didn't say he would reach out to me to ask for support, but he would warn himself that this was going to happen so it didn't hurt him as much.

And I took a step back and realized that I had not created a space where the student was able to go through something that traumatic and still succeed in my course, nor did I create a space that students felt comfortable even approaching me to say they were going through something and ask for us together to go through what support I can provide. But I had also created, in my mind, this whole story about what was going on with the student when I never even talked to them. I made so many assumptions based on their identity and my identity – about what was going on with the scenario.

And from that moment on, I decided that's not how I was going to approach my classes, because who even knows what other students I have had this kind of impact on without even having any idea what was going on. If I don't give this assignment, I have no idea what's happening. If I give this assignment and they don't feel like sharing, I've no idea what's happening.

So, why don't I create a space where I take the first step, reach out to them? Just checking in about any support I can provide? And it could be as simple as "yeah I've just been oversleeping and I'm having a hard time," or it could be something like this, something very traumatic. And I can support them by finding support on campus or support them

So, why don't I create a space where I take the first step, reach out to them? Just checking in about any support I can provide?

in the classroom by extending assignments, anything. But my role in this has to be a supporting role. It can't be a hands-off, nonchalant role, and that's something that I realized in that moment. I definitely wish I still had contact with that student, because I would let them know that I apologize, I apologize for the trauma that I inflicted, and I want them to know that I am making amends. I'm changing the way that I do things because of that experience. While I understand that does not help them in the moment, because I learned it too late, I would hope that they would at least understand that that's something I learned from them and I'm grateful for it, you know? So yeah...that was a huge, huge learning experience.

M: Your story about learning too late reminded me of another difficult experience I had with my non-grace (or anti-grace - I'm not sure yet which one). I had an experience early in my teaching career where I got frustrated at a student for missing my course for a full month. She was a mathematics education major, and had told me this prior to her absence. She attended class one day, roughly about three weeks prior to the end of the course. I saw her and asked to step out of the class to talk to her. I start by asking where she has been for a month. Before her answer, I brought up that because she wants to become a teacher, she should be an exemplary student. I said something to the effect of, "Don't you want to be the student that you want in your own classes?" She then started crying, telling me about her mother who had cancer. She had to visit her, take her to treatments, and be around her for support.

My heart sank to the floor. Again, I assumed the worst of my students, pitting them against me. I asked myself, "Why would they miss my course?," incredulously, without answering that question for myself. This was another one of many times where I learned too late, and it was a time where I had to add to my small (at the time) amount of grace. I apologized right then and there, but I wish I could apologize to her again. And again.

This is a story that I will never let go. It has pushed me towards radical grace, because I do not ever want to see that kind of disappointment in my students, nor do I ever want to feel like my heart sink again due to my own actions. There is a lot of power associated with teaching, and to see first-hand how that power can destroy students' feelings, defaulting to grace can preempt many of these negative experiences.

We never know what students are going through. With that as a baseline, we, as people of power in a course, can directly influence that stress.

These stories should be a warning to future instructors that adversarial student-teacher relationships leave both parties heart-broken. Radical grace can be a first step towards some ease of difficulty.

Chapter II

What is Radical Grace?

THE IMPETUS FOR ALL OF THIS WORK IS THIS: What is radical grace? Radical is defined as "far-reaching or thorough." Grace means "courteous goodwill." The words first combined for us in a conversation about teaching with Amanda Ruiz, a mathematician and educator. But what does this phrase mean to us?

M: Define radical grace. Because, I was thinking about this the other day. There's two words here. There's "radical," which is a descriptor for "grace." What is "grace" in your mind? And what makes what you're doing "radical"?

C: So, you know, what's really interesting is the first thing that came to mind when you said, "what is grace," I thought: forgiveness. And so I often think showing grace to yourself and to others, is to forgive yourself for current errors, for past errors, and for future errors but also forgiving other people, right? Giving them some space and support to be their full selves, un-apologetically their full selves if that makes sense.

So, that's really how I think about it. What do I need to support you, what do I need to do to support you in this space? Because I know supporting you supports me which supports you. And it's not just that selfishness – sometimes I'm helping my students to my detriment. But I think "I can do this. I can support you with the little I have and I can rebuild. But what am I breaking down if I don't come through in this moment for them?" And so I think about it in that way, and I think that's maybe where the radical comes in, because I think it's radical that you sometimes have to put yourself on the back burner.

And it's very often that people say you shouldn't do that, but I think when you set aside your needs, your viewpoint... and not in this way that, "you can have two of my kidneys and let me cut up my liver and give it to this random stranger," – it's not like that. But it's the amount of need that I have in that moment can be put aside to help the student because their need is bigger. So, helping them is, in the long run, doing more good than just thinking about myself in that moment. That's really the battle you have to have. Am I doing this to such a detriment that I won't be able to help anyone else, or is it in a way that it is okay to give a part of myself in this case?

Because we've all seen students who have math trauma... my grace has to be radical to even fight through all of that.

M: Yeah. Is part of it "radical" due to the norms of mathematics and/or academia?

C: Absolutely. I think we're at the stage where we're putting ourselves first and you're actually told, "pay yourself first," all these things, and I agree with that, to some extent. But I think we go really far, and we think about the impact that giving other people grace has on us as an individual: "But what if they take advantage, or what if they do this or that?" And you're seeing it from this side of "what is the benefit to me as an individual person and what could be the harm to me as an individual person?" Instead of the other way around: "what is the benefit to the students if I have grace here? What is the benefit, what's the harm if I don't provide grace?" and thinking about the repercussions of that in the long-term. Because we've all *seen* students who have math trauma. They come into our classrooms and they automatically were like, "I'm not going to be able to do this. I'm terrible at it." And it's because someone didn't show them grace in the past.

And now, my grace has to be radical to even fight through all of that. It sort of pushes through all of what they're saying and feeling. I have to be extra just to get them to feel comfort.

M: We're hitting a good point in the semester right now, where people are hitting things hard. It's six, seven, eight weeks in, and people are just having a hard time. And it seems like that extra push from the teacher, from us, can go such a long way. I always tell people around here – I think about it this way, if I did everything I could to help or ensure student success, then I can rest my head on a pillow after 16 weeks or even after every night going, "look, I tried my best." Whatever happens, that's on them. Not to be blame-shifting or anything like that, but I know that I tried everything I could to support them. It's so weird that is radical, right?! Because I feel like education should be a supportive experience. I think about apprenticeships, where you're trying, you have this person that wants to learn this craft from you. They're the person that's going to take over your company. Don't you want to support them? Don't you want to show them the ins and outs and everything instead of taking away?

C: It doesn't make any sense to me, except that there is this competition and it's a very weird sort of thing, and I think in this scenario it's this competition for your time. "If I give this to you then I have to give to other people and it takes all this time for me to provide this". And I get that we are time-stretched. But the impact it has on us is minimal compared to the impact it has on the student, and maybe we've forgotten that. I think we're so far from being in that space, and many of us have never been in that space. I've been in that space plenty of times, where I'm struggling and I just need a teacher or professor to reach out and just say, "hey, how are you doing? What's going on, what can I do to help?" Just to show that I'm not invisible if that makes sense. That someone sees me and they care. And I remember that, and maybe that's why I have this sort of interaction with my students, I remember what that feels like and what a difference it would have made, and I see it all the time, with my students. I'll say "hey, just checking on you". They are always grateful and say "thank you so much for reaching out" and "I really appreciate you asking this. No one has really checked on me." And their whole attitude changes in the classroom, how they interact with me, how they interact with others, and it's because they are *seen* as a whole, and we rarely do that for our students in general. Also if I can generalize, I think as a community, academics, we sometimes don't think about other stuff that can be going on outside of your classroom.

M: Unfortunately, at the end of the day, there is always other stuff. There's a grade that you have to put on a transcript that can impact scholarships, can impact internships that can impact anything future-wise. And so, as much as I tell my students don't focus on grades, they themselves can't shake that mindset. So, how do you incorporate radical grace in assessments?

C: I let students rewrite things. So after they get feedback, and they may have a better understanding of the topic or subject, I say, "you know you can rewrite this and turn it back in. We could talk about what you were thinking before, and what you're thinking now". And I think that's because we tell them all the time "learn from your mistakes" but we never give them the opportunity to show that they have. This is really the chance to do that sort of thing.

It's also really hard when you are struggling in a class at the very beginning. Then, it all sort of clicks or you get some support, and now it's starting to make sense. But you have these grades that will negatively impact your total score. That was the beginning, before you could really figure it all out. I mean if I got judged on how I am in week three with teaching, I'd be in so much trouble. I got the first week where we're just introducing, and then work comes in, and I'm behind on life already.

So this is where students also need grace. You want to give them the opportunity to go back and realize, "Oh, this was the error I made" and that be actually a benefit to them. We all know it's a benefit to them, but we're talking about grades here. We're talking about this thing that hangs over their heads. And so if we don't give them the opportunity to, you know, look things over in a way that's beneficial to them, many of them won't do it. They also have limited time.

I think about that all the time. So I do some un-grading now and I have students that talk about how they never used to read their comments or feedback. They looked at the number and put it away because that was it for them, but when you're actually not providing a letter grade but you are giving feedback, they are reading and understanding things a bit more. They're also developing as a student in your classroom. I think that's one of the ways where I think about giving grace during assessments – allowing them to actually use the assessment in the way that we hope they will.

M: That quote, that you just gave, it reminds me a lot of the negative reciprocation that happens in a classroom. Because a teacher will put "negative two" and then will put some comments. The students then are saying "oh my gosh, negative two, this is tough. I kind of don't want to see this right now. Put it away." And then the teacher sees this unfolding and goes, "well, why did I make comments in the first place?" Why do they have to look at the comments? They are distraught.

It also forces me to think about what is education. Is it about learning? Then I should give every opportunity for them to learn. No one individual has a linear learning model. I think learning is quite exponential, or should be piece-wise with exponential pieces. I think that's a huge part of this. I can recognize that each student does not learn the same at all. Each student will not be on the same page in your class, let alone on an assessment, let alone on an exam, and so forth. And can we give the necessary mechanisms for them to actually grow and learn.

I think a big question to me is: What are you learning in this class that you're going to take with you five years from now? To be honest with you, I've got two partial differential equations books up there on my shelf and I couldn't tell you one small piece of content from both of those books.

Is it about learning? Then I should give every opportunity for them to learn.

C: Heat equation. You're welcome.

M: HA! Thank you. To me, the content matters less and less in classrooms. It's more about *process*. All of our content is readily available to many at their fingertips, but how do we understand it? How do we synthesize it? This is a tough thing.

The second thing I think about is the grace we give does not have to be reciprocated. But the more we give it, the more opportunity there is for students to reciprocate it. What if I lost somebody? What if I was sick for two weeks bedridden? We're in a pandemic: what if my family was impacted? I know that my students care. But the level of care, I think, would shift due to the amount of grace that we've already set up in the classroom. That set-up may take a while, and it requires that I be open and vulnerable about my life events – again, the students have to trust that you are not "against" them but rather supporting them and wanting them to succeed. So, for some students, it may be the first day, but for others, longer, and I've got to be OK with all of that.

C: I think you may not actually ever need them to reciprocate that grace to you, but they'll show it to others, they'll show it to themselves. And I think that there always needs to be more grace in this space, because we're all struggling. We are all struggling. There are very few of us out here not having any trouble at all. So the idea that we can be *that* for each other, that grace, that forgiveness, letting us be ourselves unapologetically, our whole selves in spaces, is very wonderful. We just see so much happen when we can be honest and say how we feel instead of holding it in because this is not the time or the space to have this conversation and to do these things, or have these feelings, as if we're not human.

When I first started teaching at the University of San Diego (USD), my dad passed away. And so I was devastated, but then it was around a week before the end of school, and I was like, "I think I have to go back because I don't know how my students are going to feel going into finals without me." Which is a wild thought, I know! But we had gone through whole semester together and I wanted to be there with them. So I went back, and it was way too early and I shouldn't have gone back, and I realized that now. But they gave me a card – these students that I just had, for that time. They all signed this card for me, they gave it to me, and I was just like, "oh my gosh." They *thought* about this, and it's very easy to just be like, "we're going to pass this card around sign it," and then no one does. Then you just don't give it to me, or the one person who bought it gives it to me right, and says, "hey, thought about you," but they all signed this card, and it made such a difference. I was saying to myself, "Okay, I know I shouldn't be back here but... I am here, and I can be okay here." If I needed to leave the classroom for a minute because I'm crying because they just gave me this card, they will understand because they get it. They're not going to be like, "what's going on with you? Why are you not here?" I was very honest with them with what was happening with me.

I try to be as honest and transparent with my students as much a possible, because I need them to know I'm a full person. And if I disappear for a day because something has happened, I want you to know that it's, not because I don't want to be here, something has happened. And I think it's important for you to know that I'm not just living in my office until it's time to teach, and then I walk over there, and then I go back to my office and wait for you to show up. I have other stuff, and because I have other stuff, I know you have other stuff. And so, when this other stuff isn't working the way we hope it is, we're going to give each other grace around it and support each other, because it makes all the difference to know that you're seen.

M: Yeah! You've got other stuff, I've got other stuff. Math is forty-seventh on the list.

C: Listen!!! Math is such a small percentage, you know?!

M: But it's.. it's really tough. Because some students have had previous situations where it has been only number one. And you can't do anything else, and you're not allowed to do anything else. And they see it, and they feel it. They know when you're not being genuine about that grace and care. But when it does hit, when it does click, it's *amazing*.

You know I... I haven't seen a student for a week, and I emailed the student, and the student, you know emailed me twice, and in the next morning said to me, "it meant a lot to me." I also had another student that I emailed, and they said, "thank you" and everything else, and I haven't seen them since. And "previous me" would have been really hurt by that. Devastated. But now that's the grace that's coming in – that grace that's saying, "look, this person is having difficulties." And it happens, it happens with life. That's not about me. It's not the class, it's not this – it's them having difficulties.

C: And even if it is your class, you can't do anything about it until that person reaches out and asks for you to do something about it. But what you have done is let them know that you are open to that. That's really the only thing you can change in a moment. I think we often think that this student just doesn't like me and is doing this because of me, and that's where we forget that the students or other people in general are whole human beings. It's not just this one thing for them. And it could be, it could be they don't like your class... it could be, right? But the *assumption* that it's that? We just go to a default of, "well, they just don't care, why should I care?" and it's like...

M: Negative feedback loop.

C: Yep negative feedback! There you go.

M: It's the negative of radical grace.

C: Okay!? Look at you!

We can see that radical grace is more than a definition. It is the willingness to understand students are coming in with math trauma, that we do not need to compete with them or with each other, and that a focus on process and revision can have incredible consequences. Radical grace looks like honesty and transparency with students, since we are all whole people with lives – difficulties and successes.

Chapter III

What about Equality and Equity?

AN IMPORTANT PART OF THIS WORK IS TO acknowledge that none of this work happens on a level playing field. Not for us as instructors and not for our students.

C: When I was at a previous institution, there was a male colleague who said they "didn't understand the difference between equity and equality." So, you know, we shared the picture with the fence and the boxes (see Figure 1a), and they said "but this is just a picture." So, at that point, I was like, "oh, this person actually doesn't really want to know. They're pretending to not understand because they are quite smart. They are pretending they don't get this, but, okay." And so, then I saw this one picture describing the difference with bicycles right, and you have people with different bodies and they all have the same bicycle and it's like that doesn't work and then equity is them getting the bicycle that fits them (see Figure 1b).

Okay, so I thought, "this might be a better illustration," because when I showed my colleague the one with the boxes, his response was

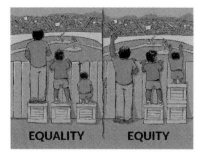 

(a) Interaction Institute for Social Change (Artist: Angus Maguire)   (b) 2017 Robert Wood Johnson Foundation

Figure 1: Two illustrations to describe the difference between equity versus equality. (Edited to gray scale by authors)

"why don't you just put all the boxes out there and then people can take only the boxes that they need?" To which I responded, "because people will take more boxes than what they need. And what if I need a different kind of box?"

So my idea or analogy is this: Imagine a teeter-totter, if you will, where one side is heavier than the other. And we can think about what heavy means like more things or less, more burdens or more privileges, and equity is putting the fulcrum, or the item holding the teeter-totter above ground, in the center of mass to balance it out where equality is to put the fulcrum in the middle of the teeter-totter. Folks are saying "Let's put it in the middle," but we are misunderstanding that some folks have more, and that's not balanced. We need to put it where the center of mass is to support those that don't have what they need. Either they have too many burdens or not enough resources, and so we're lifting them up to support them more. So we are balancing them out with those that have a lot, whatever way we want to do it, but I was just like, "that's what equity is."

It is this idea of balancing things out. So this idea of "what is fair" is that the teeter-totter *never* starts balanced. And we have to remember that. Until it does start balanced, we can't put the fulcrum in the middle. You can't. We have got to figure out where to place it so that we can create balance.

M: Okay, so I think about a lot about spirited debates about student loan debt. And like this question about "should we write off or give people $10,000 off their student loan debt?" And how many people have talked to me about it like "Well, I went through student loan debt, so they should." Listen, I went through student loan debt. I paid it off. And I would *love* for other people to have $ 10,000 off their student loan debt. I don't understand this notion of burdening others... because you were burdened. Not giving others grace because you weren't given grace.

C: And you overcame it, right? I mean, if anything, that is more reason to give grace because you're perpetuating why grace is important. As opposed to creating more people who are like "well I didn't get that, so why should you?" versus "yeah,

> *So this idea of "what is fair" is that the teeter-totter never starts off balanced.*

you know what? I got that and you should too, because it made things so much better for me. It made things better for me as a whole person". Or even, "I didn't get this, and it would have made things better, so let me give it to you so you don't have to struggle like I did."

I had to take qualifying exams in graduate school. Did you? Did you enjoy it? Was that pleasurable? Not at all. So why would you put someone through that pain that you went through, right? Are we trying to make things better for the people after us? I had to struggle. Do you want everyone to struggle, because you did? Like it's so weird to me.

M: So this brings me to my second part when I think about equity versus equality. So there's those that are like, "I struggled through this so you should too," but there's another camp that– and to use your qualifiers analogy– that didn't struggle through qualifying exams. So why should it be changed? Do you know what I'm saying? "This is nothing to me, so why, why is it so hard for others?" Or even "I didn't have student loan debt. So why should other people take $10,000 off theirs?" So those are the two groups of individuals that I have a hard time with.

C: I think also that there are people who don't think certain people deserve it. There are some people undeserving of grace in their eyes. They worry that people will "take advantage" of this thing. So then its like, "I'm going to make sure no one gets it, even though I really need it. But if it were a thing then people would take advantage, so no one gets it."

M: We need a whole, we need a whole book chapter and a whole podcast about "take advantage". And how it seems like a personal affront. It's part of the "breaking trust" thing right? If someone took advantage of you, then what happens? They get a rest? They get an assignment grade? One person *may* take advantage, but twelve students will look at the grace given and change their lives. And, from personal experience, will commit more of themselves into the class.

Equity versus equality comes up so much in our work as those interested in restorative justice. Much of the remedial work comes in the form of creating equality, but it leaves so many issues unanswered and often provides a scapegoat for those who do not want to do the work. The idea of a fulcrum and the center of mass helps to illustrate for us the difference between equity and equality. We hope that this also provides a visual on how the work of restorative justice has to be founded in ideas of equity and not just in ideas of equality.

Chapter IV

What does Radical Grace look like in the Classroom?

THERE ARE MANY PHILOSOPHICAL considerations when implementing radical grace. We must think about why we are providing grace in the classroom. But we can believe in radical grace without implementing radical grace. This chapter gives concrete actions that the two of us have taken in the classroom that anyone can consider in implementation.

M: Is it active learning, or the way I'm teaching, that necessitates radical grace? Or is it that radical grace pushes me into more active learning? I'm wondering how this relationship is. If I were lecturing, would I need radical grace at all?

C: I think that if you were lecturing, radical grace shows up in a different way. This is what I meant when I discussed this idea of a "toggle" with you recently. Because radical grace isn't just a teaching style. It is a full philosophy more than anything. When I come into this class, how do I interact with my students?

So you can have a large lecture or a lecture style class and how you talk about the material with your students shows this grace. How you think about the questions you're asking your students to work on. How you interact with them outside of the classroom. Right? All of that, I think, is where you can see radical grace, because what we're talking about with radical grace is that we trust them and we asked them to trust us.

We work on this material together, but also outside of that classroom space we have honest conversations with them and give them grace when they need it and even when they don't. There's just always grace and that could look like many things— more time on assignments, presenting in the classroom if they're like, "oh we're still struggling with this topic," then you're like, "okay yeah let's go back to it" instead of "that's not on my schedule".

I think that is what grace can look like. I don't think grace looks like one thing because it depends on the students. Look at the population of students you're working with and support them as whole people.

Do you have to have your classroom space just to be like everyone is talking at the same time and it's so lovely? No. For the topic you're talking about, that may not work. That may not work for that population of students. You could have a very quiet classroom.

You don't have to teach your courses in some specific pedagogical way and I think that is what some people are missing when we talk about radical grace. It needs to be said that this is our philosophy on teaching. And that it looks different in each of our classrooms. The analogy I like to use is that I'm pushing you out of a window but I'm giving you a parachute. You are going to be free-falling, but please know you are supported. Instead of just like, "Well, this is the way it works. I'm not going to explain to you why it works." So, let's have a conversation about what we're doing in the classroom space because I respect you as a whole person. And I will talk to you with transparency about it.

And sure the certain way that I feel most comfortable teaching is using active teaching. But some people don't feel that way, but we can both have radical grace in the classroom.

M: I think that that's part of the the grace is the transparency of what you're believing in. But, it seems to me that it's needed early on.

C: Right away, yes.

M: Either right away or within those first few weeks. There's a certain kind of interplay that goes on in those first few weeks where you and the students are getting to know each other. It's not going to happen week 10. Because by that time everybody has set up these unwritten rules. Right? It's something where it's got to be early on. Set up the class early on. It has been a huge eye-opening experience to talk to people, to learn what other instructors do in those first few days or weeks, and to keep modifying what I'm going to say at the beginning of the semester. But I know that I need to say things. Not only say things, but to get them thinking about what it is that is needed for those first few days that counts for the rest of the semester. I borrowed it from somebody, I don't know, their name is Candice Price, but anyways...

This notion of anti-competitiveness. It is now bar-none, one of the first things I'm going to do for the rest of my time. Because I saw it in work. I swear either a conversation or something I saw on your syllabus that was saying "Look, we need to have a talk about how competitiveness destroys what we're trying to do here". We're not on a bell curve. I've always hated curving. I felt like it did nothing for learning. Competitiveness does not do anything for learning. What are we doing that's going to help all of us in terms of learning? Right? Another thing, oh my God, it goes into radical grace, but it also goes into like, "What are our values versus our beliefs"

A lot of people have this "drop an exam" policy. And to me that's beautiful, because it gives grace, but every one of my policies or every one of my assessments I hope to incorporate some mathematical learning with it. So, my thing is, you can have a drop or some kind of policy, but can they learn from those exams that they took? So how can they learn from the exams that they took and get a drop policy? Well, I have them redo their exams for the drop policy, and almost everybody takes this and almost everybody learns a little bit from what they did from that last exam.

C: Oh I like that!

M: And if they need more time that's not a big deal, like the big deal to me is, "how are you learning from this?" Here's another metaphor. Let's throw this out: homework is our practices, quizzes are the scrimmage, and the tests are the games. Okay, and to me, giving you that option of going over your exam for for future changes? That to me is going over game film. And even during the scrimmages, which are the quizzes, I have in my classes, I'll literally stop them and I'll be like, "okay, I messed up (jokingly), it wasn't supposed to be an individual quiz. Go ahead and get into groups." And then I'll stop them again: "oh my gosh, what do you get for number two?" And to me that's me stopping the scrimmage in the middle of the scrimmage and going "Look, we need to figure out a way to channel the ball to our wings and we are playing the ball in the middle way too much. So focus on trying to get it outside." I can do that, in the middle of a scrimmage.

I think that... I don't know... this focus on grades has just like muddled everything to a "I have to do this, I have to do that, I have to do this" mentality. You don't have to do anything. You're using standards-based grading, you're using un-grading. That immediately tells me I can shift my policies. I can shift my values. I can shift all this.

C: Yes! I think that I love the analogy. I think I love the analogy of the practice-scrimmage-game. I think we often think about learning as an individual sport. That's where the competitiveness comes in. Right!? Like "I alone have to do this and so I am only good if I'm better than the person next to me". Because there can only be one winner instead of thinking about us being a team and us crossing the finish line together or us, you know, scoring together and working together to do all these things. We can definitely try and think about it like that.

I think that is what the shift needs to be because learning is not actually done on the individual level. Even if you by yourself prove something in mathematics or write an essay, you're not working alone. You're are likely using

Why can't we celebrate all those different strengths?

someone's work or someone's influence as your foundation. No one is sitting by themselves in a room and thinking "I thought this thing all on my own. I'm going to write it down." No. You thought about this thing because you read all this other work or pieced together things you know or you're talking about your ideas with someone else. And I think that's the part we have to remember is that we are not working solo. And us showing that in the classroom space is important. So I think about when people ask "but how do I know what they know as an individual" when I talk about collaboration in the classroom, I think, "well actually you never do." You don't actually know what they know as an individual. What you know is what you have shown them, what someone has shown them, and hopefully what they have built from that knowledge. Why can't we see what we know as a collective working together? Because we all have different strengths that we're bringing to the table, so why can't we celebrate all those different strengths?

M: Or even we all have things that we'd like to improve?

C: Yes!

M: And how can we, how can we leverage one strength to help with the other one.

C: Yes! This!

M: It brings me to the first time, one of the first few times that I talked with Gail Tang, another friend and math professor. She gave a presentation about how she did group work. She would have quizzes that were on just one piece of paper and a problem that they had to work one as a group. But... they couldn't talk. And each of them had a different colored pen. So you saw the individual prompts and ideas, but you also saw them working on the collective whole. I need to include more collective parts into my tests. I've done this one where I have a prompt and they have to make up answers towards those prompts. They can leverage each other's answers to make up a new one prompt. I think that this is a big deal.

You can see a lot where somebody's grace comes into play. You can see radical grace from your students. How there are certain prompts on my tests, where I say "Dr. Savić did this problem, this integral. Can you give feedback on Dr. Savić's work, and how can you support Dr. Savić in improving his process?"

And they provide the most beautiful comments! "Oh, I really appreciated how Dr. Savić did it in this way" or "It was different from my way, but Dr. Savić got stuck on this part and may need to improve on this." I like that I see their grace in how to handle of a fictional problem. And to me that's beautiful because it. It really reinforces the grace to others.

C: Yeah. It's very funny because we did something similar on our calculus final. It says something like, "this person did this problem incorrectly. What is the one question you would ask them to help them find their error?" And some of the comments/answers were not actually helpful: "Why don't you know how to do these kinds of problems by now?" Hahaha they didn't hold back.

M: Sometimes it might be people looking at themselves in the mirror.

C: Oh yes! And that part, with us talking about radical grace to ourselves, ourselves as instructors, we can talk about ourselves with grace as instructors but also we're allowing... "allowing" sounds weird but "giving?"... I want to say we're giving the students permission to be graceful to themselves. We're opening the door to letting them know that they deserve grace. They deserve to show grace to themselves, because we all do so much negative talk.

> *We're opening the door to letting them know that they deserve grace.*

And we're helping them hear another voice that says: "You're doing great!" "Look at you, you're doing wonderful!" "It's okay. Take your time. Take the time that you need." And we're letting them know that it is okay because we can all be so negative sometimes. We speak so negatively to ourselves. Do you think it is because part of the culture of academia is to not normalize being "mediocre" or something like that?

M: Yes, we've normalized not to make mistakes.

C: Right! It's not okay to make mistakes.

M: I've told students multiple times. And they've been like "Thank you! Thank you so much for allowing me to have this extension." I say "okay, you're welcome. I just want you to reflect on this and think about what you can do for others. Because with me it is fine."

How can you extend this kindness that you feel like you've received to others? I think that is a gigantic part of radical grace, yes, the permeating of "paying it forward".

C: Yes it goes back to breaking trust, not even worrying about what that student is doing but rather, like you put it, providing opportunity for students to reflect on their own grades. And its very nice that a student says "Hey, thank you." And I want to see people putting into action what they believe, what they value. So yeah I think: what are our actions? And how are they being implemented and how are they providing grace?

We wanted to share with you ways that we have implemented radical grace in the classroom. Not to shame or to provide a blueprint, but to provide examples. Please note that while we are starting from the same philosophy and theory, we, the authors, have diversity in our actions and practices. It is important to see that radical grace can show up differently in any classroom. This means that our actions can not be stagnant. They have to be dynamic, even with in the same classroom space and semester. This allows us to provide "just in time" grace.

Chapter V

How do we show Radical Grace to Ourselves and Others?

GRACE CAN BE PROVIDED, but it's a sense of trust that allows for it to grow. This conversation is dedicated to fostering trust within our classrooms. The same trust can be co-created within our academic spaces and, ultimately, our lives. This conversation started off with talking about colleagues that substitute for us in our classes.

M: Who around me has the kind of grace and patience in the class and outside that can take it over for even a day?

C: Yeah because I think about it – when I'm gone, what is the impact that person has on my students? Because they have to teach some of this topic. And so it's like, "Okay, how are they going to do this?" I still don't feel comfortable with someone proctoring an exam for me because I feel like my students will see me up there and I'll be calm. And they'll ask me a question and the way I answer them is usually, "you're doing great. Look, you've got this piece here, you have this piece, you just have to figure out this part. It's similar to something we've done before so sit and take some time to think about what this looks like." Something before "you got this" right, that sort of calm voice, because often it's like they're panicking. It's not that they don't know what they're doing. It's panicking.

You know the person who's proctoring for me isn't going to know this person, isn't going to know that the student does actually know this work. So what kind of feedback are they going to be able to give them?

M: I don't know. It's trust - they trust you, don't know this other person, and you've established six weeks together. For the most part if you're in radical grace by day one, by week six there's even these inklings that people have that are like, "he's with me."

C: Yeah, *we're* with them. I had a student I was talking to because we have these reflection questions in the homework, and I read one from an international student. She said "it's very frustrating because I've taken this class before, but I'm struggling because I don't understand the language." So I met with her and she was like, "You know what? Just you meeting with me lets me know that you care. You're on my side, and I can come to you and ask you questions. I already felt that way, but now I really know that." And it was just like all because of a sense of "what can I do to support you?" Right? I was talking about feet in class: LeBron James is six feet tall. She said, "what is that in centimeters?" I have no idea. And I should. Because I'm assuming that I'm using a universal language here, and in fact centimeters is probably the universal language I should be using.

> *"You know what? Just you meeting with me lets me know that you care."*

M: You know, it's interesting you say that. Because I have a new conjecture: *Radical creativity is radical grace, and radical grace is contagious.* Because my teaching assistant came up to me today and said, "this student has had a few missing homework assignments and I haven't seen her in class. Should we check up on her?" I don't know if this TA had heard about grace and caring in math before, but I think that this teaching assistant had no experience with teaching prior to this. And just that reaching out to me... What he didn't know was that 10 minutes prior to that at the end of the exam I came outside and talked with her one on one. Asked how she was and everything else and offered as much as I could in any capacity that I'm trained to do. And so it's awesome that he independently was worried and wanted to check in. That to me was just a gigantic moment today.

The students are being very critical. They may be thinking very deeply about why I'm going out to only talk to this one person.

I also did a technique where it wasn't me going out to her specifically to check on her. What I did was I, because it was our exam today and people were getting done early, I exited and talked to everybody outside of the classroom. It's because any action that a teacher takes is being looked at. It's being examined in some way. I really appreciate doing it, because the students were being very critical. They may be thinking very deeply about why I'm going out to only talk to this one person. So I've got to anticipate and go, "Okay, I need to do this with all so that she doesn't feel a certain way and so everybody else doesn't think or feel certain ways about her."

C: That's huge, Miloš. It's just that slight change, right? It's not like there's something with you, and everyone else is fine. It's like, "I'm checking up on everyone because I care about everyone.

M: Think about it. There are two decisions: ignore everyone or check up on every one, right? Because I wanted to make sure that you know, a couple of people were doing well.

C: You know the thing is, *we can only see so much*. So while there are two students that you really wanted to check on, you're giving yourself and the students an opportunity to check in on each of them. So, while the student could be having a difficult time, and you just don't notice it, in this moment, you're creating a chance for them to say, "you know actually I am struggling." Because there are certain times when you find out later that a student had something going on, or they're struggling and you didn't know because you couldn't see it.

We should really be trying to give our students these opportunities to tell us what support they need. It's very hard, though. There's this vulnerability, especially if you don't have the trust. If there's no trust, the student could think, "that person won't care, will use it against me later, or will bring it up in class."

M: All those can be deterrents. It could also be a deterrent that you, as the instructor, don't want to open yourself up to all of this. But, I think one of the things that I've realized, that is felt through radical grace for myself, is that I'm not superhuman. I have huge areas of growth that I need to recognize and go, "hey, this is not my area right here." And find those avenues for them to go to professionals. I am not versed in any kind of mental health guidance or anything. I can tell you what *I* do, but it's not necessarily the same as others. Everybody's got their own different ways of going about their lives.

I think that's something I had to do myself. I had to go through stages. Dr. Savić 1.0 was in denial. It was just like, "Okay, people struggle. That's it." Dr. Savić 2.0 was like, "everything's on me." I have to do everything.

I have to do all this. I have to eat and bear all of the difficulties that students have. Try to solve everything on my own at all times. Dr. Savić 3.0? I'm glad I got the upgrade. It's me being more comfortable with what I know and what I don't know. Recognizing how much time I can dedicate to all of that.

C: Right because you can do more harm if you don't know what you're doing. You can do more harm if you don't actually have the time to support someone in the way that they need. So we have to be conduits and not just the end-all, be-all. I can see that there's some stuff going on. You're talking with me. Let's find some support.

Because you're right - none of us are superhuman. We cannot do it all.

There are certain things we can help with. "Oh, the problem is you didn't distribute the negative." We can even have these conversations about future plans and we can share our own personal stories. But in the end... we are not trained to do everything.

So there have to be other people that we know we're connected with that we can connect them to. I think a lot of people do turn away from supporting students because they're like, "Well, I'm not trained to do that. I don't have to do that." We're not even asking you that. We're asking you to be a person or a space that a student can go to to say I need help

We're asking you to be a person or a space that a student can go to to say I need help and then you can help them find that help.

and then you can help them find that help. That's a huge impact that we could be having because there's so much to navigate as an institution. If you've been there long enough, you know all the little pockets, you know the right people to ask, the right people to talk to, and who to connect them with. And that is a skill that we all can do. We all have that skill.

We can't do it all and we shouldn't.

M: What you said about trying, but only making it worse, reminds me of the paper that Estrella Johnson and her colleagues have that shares that inquiry does not guarantee equity in teaching. If perhaps done incorrectly, it can actually exacerbate inequities in an inquiry-based or active-learning classroom.

How did you come to the realization that you knew what you knew and you knew what you didn't know? The same thing I said about my version 3.0. What version are you at? And how did you get to that point? How did you upgrade?

C: I don't even know what number I'm on. I think every year I upgrade. Every year, I learned something new, either from my friends, my colleagues, my students, and I think, "that would help this be better." I really do try to listen to my students, my friends, and colleagues about what I'm doing in the classroom and what I'm doing outside of the classroom to impact what's happening in the classroom. So it is a constant reflection.

I even make changes in the semester, right? I think we all do. The way we say things, the way we organize our classes once we've met the students… We are like, "OK. What this class needs is extra time on their own before putting them into groups to think through the problem on their own. You know, before I throw them in with people who perhaps finished it already and just want to keep moving. I've seen that it really helps, and sometimes I forget to start a class off like that and then I see that I need to and I pivot.

I don't know if this is just like imposter syndrome really rearing its head, but I always feel like I can improve, and I don't think it hurts me to think that way. I feel like I'm doing a terrible job this semester, because I'm overloaded and just overworked and I can tell that I could be better at certain things. And then you know my friends will be like, "You're probably doing amazing and your students can't even tell that you're not doing your best." I can tell that sometimes they need a little bit more, and I don't have it in me, but then after this conversation we just had, it's important to know that I can't do everything. I'm giving them the best that I have right now that I can get them and that's important.

And they know that I constantly ask them for forgiveness. And they give me that grace because they know I give it to them. They're watching this sort of thing, and so it is contagious.

I would say that I was changing little by little, and then it wasn't until I started really hearing what the students were saying that I started making "drastic" change. By giving them these reflections or asking certain questions so that they would tell me about their experience that I learned that I need to do this more. I needed to be checking in with them way more than I was. I need to know how things are going, not just at the end with evaluations or grades. And that was when I think I really started making adjustments. I was doing these sort of mid-semester reviews. "Let's just do a quick poll: How's the day going? How is the class?" And even at that point, the middle of the semester, it can be too late for some students.

Students can see the radical grace we are providing and may reciprocate to us or to others. Trust is key when thinking about us providing radical grace, but we have to remember that it's a privilege to assume good intentions. Also, we must show radical grace to ourselves and recognize that, if we want to provide radical grace, we are in a continuous state of reflection. This helps us find ways of improving our teaching, which can open opportunities for more radical grace.

Chapter VI

Teaching to Swim
Candice Price

M Y MOM AND I LEARNED HOW TO SWIM in very different ways. My mom was born in 1955 and grew up in New York City. My mother was taught to swim by her father. To teach her to swim, he threw her into the ocean. Yes, the literal Atlantic ocean. This was in hopes that her instincts would kick in and she would figure out how to swim. With no floaties, no guidance, and no support. She had to learn to swim to survive. The result was that my mom panicked. She managed to swim, only so that she could get away from her father. She was terrified of him. And while my mother did eventually learn to swim, and loved to swim, she always has a fear that stems from that first experience. The fear of not having the right support or ability to survive.

Fast forward a few years to my mom raising three children in Sacramento, California. She wanted to take us to the public pool during the hot summers but wanted to make sure we were safe around the water. So my mom signed us up for swim lessons. Every week, we went to the pool and had guided lessons. We learned how to float, how to feel comfortable putting our heads underwater, learned how to doggy paddle as well as freestyle, and we learned how to breathe when swimming. Because of this experience, my siblings and I were on our high school swim team and played water polo. We were not the best swimmers, none of us were headed to the Olympics, but we loved being in the water. We had little fear and were able to expand our skills from doggy paddle to butterfly stroke.

I often think about these two experiences in learning when I think about how I teach. It leads me to ask myself the following: Am I teaching my students to feel comfortable with the material/task or am I pushing them out there and hoping for the best? Am I teaching them to swim, or am I letting them drown? My ideas around support can sometimes seem radical. I think about my students as whole people, with lives outside of my classroom that I know nothing about. I try my best to not assume what they need but I let them know that I am there to support them. Sometimes this looks like providing them with floaties — extensions on a due date for an assignment, spending a bit more time during office hours, asking for feedback on how things are going in a course– and sometimes it looks like letting them swim– asking the questions that push on their boundaries of knowledge, fostering their creativity, having a tough discussion on work/life balance. But no matter what, I want this experience to be rooted in trust, compassion, and grace.

Am I teaching them to swim, or am I letting them drown?

Our students often come to us already knowing how to doggy paddle. It can sometimes be a survival mechanism. It is how many of us have survived being pushed into the ocean over and over again, class after class. I do not want to be just be another person pushing them into the ocean. How many times have they been shoved in by the time they get to us? What is the residual effect of that on their relationship with water? And the trauma is not just fear of water, but fear of drowning because there is no support... or even possibly the harm of being held under.

How many times have they been shoved in by the time they get to us?

In seeing my students as whole people, I acknowledge the fact that people can handle stress and trauma differently than others. And this management of stress or trauma should not decide who enjoys mathematics. It is my goal that they will venture out, knowing they have support. Knowing that they have someone who will not just watch them drown. I want to show what it looks and feels like to help someone learn to swim. To support them as they test the water, especially those who have been traumatized by the experience before.

Chapter VII

How would you Describe the "Little Grace"?

The experiences we have, the places and people we interact with, they change us. It might be small, it might be enormous, but it is, and always will be, a change. This conversation centered around the stories that made a difference in finding and fostering our own radical grace, focusing on the small actions that create a large impact.

M: So we need to talk about the little grace that occurs.

C: Right. The minutia.

M: Yeah, the day to day, the minute-to-minute interactions that happen in a classroom. Because I think that it's one of those things where students actually build the global grace from those little interactions. That's where the trust occurs. When they see those, those little actions that you're doing that shows your grace, it goes forward, and it makes this environment.

C: I think it reinforces what you've been telling them your class is going to be like. When you show the grace day-to-day, and not just in the first day, and you're saying, "I'm gonna show you grace," and then throughout the semester, you are... right? It definitely reinforces your teaching philosophy when it's in everything you do. It's not a "checkboxes" thing – it's actually who you are as an instructor. As a person.

M: So, what's an example of a small amount of grace? What do you think is radical, even in those small moments?

C: It's interesting, too, because I think we're saying small, and they're not small. Like, I think they're very exciting things that happen in our classroom spaces. However, they are small on a timescale. I think that's what we're thinking – not small actions that are in-the-minute and you're just like, "oh, my gosh, this great thing happened."

Often, I think I see it with my students, when they feel comfortable to just shout out answers or questions. And not shout out in like a disrespectful way, whatever that means, but they were engaged, and they're asking questions that were wondering about the content. "And what about this? And can I ask about this?" What you've created is a space where they feel comfortable. One student asking whatever they're curious about, knowing that you're not going to say, "that's not a part of today's lesson," or "that's taking up too much time." But also, they have this courage to say what they're thinking in front of their classmates. It's not something they're just waiting to talk to you about after class or in office hours. It's something they feel comfortable enough to even

> *I think I see [radical grace] with my students, when they feel comfortable to just shout out answers or questions.*

say in front of everyone. Because you've all decided to give each other grace in that time.

M: Courteous goodwill, right. Why is the opposite the norm? It's my biggest question. It's the hardest question.

C: Discourteous bad-will.

M: HA! But it's true, right!? How can it be the norm that we ask questions a bunch? How can it become the norm that you just say what you're thinking about in terms of your mathematics? Your content? And then it's not taken and misconstrued into something really bad.

This professor said, "you couldn't be more wrong." I decided at that very moment: "This is not a class I will be speaking in."

C: Yeah, I have a horror story about something like this. I think maybe this was undergrad, but I had this professor in statistics. It's day one, and he's asking students questions like, "What is this?" And he asked us some question, which I know I blocked because of the trauma. But he asked the class a question and students raised their hand and they answered, and this professor said, "you couldn't be more wrong." I decided at that very moment: "This is not a class I will be speaking in." He didn't have grace in that moment to talk to a student in a way that encouraged being "brave" to ask questions, but also to be brave to be wrong. Also, to feel comfortable asking this question so that you know *why* you are wrong. Versus "I'm just going to keep my wrong thoughts to myself because I'm too afraid to be wrong. Even my right thoughts, I'll never know if what I was thinking or my intuition is good or correct because I'm too afraid to even ask." It is obviously a memory that has stuck with me.

M: It didn't even happen to you either. I think that's a big deal, those little moments of grace, or the opposite, can have this ripple effect that goes well beyond just the teacher-to-student interaction. You had that interaction, and I guarantee you almost every student that we interact with has had that same kind of situation happen to them.

C: Oh, guaranteed, because it's the norm of how we interact with students. Maybe not those exact words, but some way of shutting down the curiosity, some way of shutting down the attempt. "I'm just going to try. And maybe I'll fall on my face, but at least I will be helped back up," or at least someone will be like, "that was a really good try. Maybe if you tried this instead," or, "okay, let's move on with that thought and what are we really thinking?" Are we diving deeper into my question, so that we can actually think about "what is the confusion?" Giving me the opportunity to learn and to grow? To fall down and pick myself up?

M: Yeah. All of this makes me think about anti-deficit thinking or asset-based instruction, both of which are framed differently. I just keep thinking about students, especially those who have gone through so much of what you've said, the scenarios that you've said, and they want to answer or do something in my class out-loud to everybody. There's got to be some kind of both mathematical reason and motivation to do it. The binary choice of "you're right," or "you're wrong," seeps through. But, I'm now in the mode of: "how did you think that? Guide me through that?" When you start unpacking those layers, there's some beautiful thought and beautiful motivation that came through, coupled with some practices

> *When you start unpacking those layers, there's some beautiful thought and beautiful motivation that came through, coupled with some practices and skills that I would want any student to have.*

and skills that I would want any student to have. But that's only there because I asked the question that I was genuinely curious about. There's also a co-created space centered around grace in front of everybody to say "where did this come from?"

C: Right. And the encouragement to ask, "Whoa, what is that even from?" That's such a different way to ask. "Can you tell me how you got to that? This is really cool. I see what you're thinking." And I mean, most of the time, we can figure it out. *If we want to.* But, if we have blinders on? We're like, "oh, no, that's completely wrong. You just do it this way." Then we've shut out all this creativity that our students may have.

As an aside to this, sometimes my students will say something like, "But one day you said this," and then I can be like "I did. And this is great that you remember that. But that was for one particular situation. Do we remember the situation that that was for?" And we get to recall things because it's in their minds. But now we get to connect these ideas. "What's different about this case?" So they can actually look for similarities and differences, patterns, which is what we think about so much with mathematics. But if I had just shut a student down and said, "No, that's completely wrong," without getting an opportunity to see where that thought process came from, how do I help them make connections?

M: It's those micro-actions, those little bits, those in-the-moment ideas. And to be honest, I'm doing a lot of unlearning. And that's a common theme, with our book and with our podcasts is that we're kind of unpacking a lot of stuff that has been the norm. One of the things that I've learned is that gut reaction, the wincing when somebody comes in with something that's not correct will be noticed. Instead, I've learned to really trust that they're coming from a place of pure creative or problem-solving thought, that they're really coming to us with their thinking and their connection making. Could you imagine having an art exhibit and someone coming in and saying, "No, that's wrong."

C: This is not how Picasso would do it.

M: I think there's not that much of a difference between mathematics or any topic and art, especially with the process. It's those small little actions that can create so much. I saw today many different students participate in class. But, I bet you that if it went another way, it could have been shut down to one or two students that participated in the whole class.

C: Which has happened.

M: And students are machine learning in a way in your class. They're taking data points from minute five, and going, "Oh, okay. You know what, I can throw this out there." Or the opposite reaction.

C: Exactly. Yeah. Today is not a day where I will speak up, right? Because I can see the bits of grace that are not showing up that day. I'm going to take in that data, exactly what you said, and decide, "this is not a safe day to speak or to ask questions." You're gonna have students that never think about that, and no matter what data they're getting, their questions will be asked. I'm not just teaching that student. I'd like all my students to have days where they feel like they could ask questions, or at least me not be the hindrance for them. Everybody has stuff going on. I'm not saying everybody has to talk every day. But I don't want it to be me that keeps them from talking. I don't want it to be the classroom environment that keeps them from talking.

M: Why do we have to put adjectives to space? Like safe space? Brave space? Should those be baked into the word "space?" When you're in my class, you're with a class. I feel like that's where the "norm" thing comes in to place. We have to have this discussion about brave spaces or safe spaces. But that's because the norm, because of the radical aspect.

C: The radical part says you have to add the word "safe". Because the default is not safe.

M: Otherwise you wouldn't have to be so explicit. These little things make such a huge mark, not only in the moment, not only within the day, but also within the whole 16-week semester, year, anytime they interact with you afterwards, etc.

The radical part says you have to add the word "safe." Because the default is not safe.

C: How they interact with each other? You see a lot of moments where they're just like looking at each other and say "Go ahead". "Oh no! You go ahead." "No, no! You've got this!" Supporting each other by not commenting like "Oh, she's wrong, the answer is..." But actually more of "I am unclear how they got that answer because I have something different." Giving that person the opportunity to say, "oh, yeah, I see my error. I should have said this." Right, as opposed to, "that's wrong. That's not it." Students are very good sometimes at not correcting each other. I think I also need to give them time to share why that person is incorrect. Versus being like, "who agrees with Sally? No one? OK" Instead, I can say, "confirmation or something different?" At no point am I saying that Sally is incorrect, and I say it almost infrequently. Sally could be right and could be wrong.

Sometimes I say it when only one person has been speaking for a bit. Sometimes I say it when Sally is correct. So there isn't this like, "Oh, if Dr. Price has asked this to Sally, then it's wrong. They get the opportunity to say, "Oh, I confirm," or they say, "Well I got this and I'm not sure how they're different." And sometimes I'll work it out to show them. "Okay, so what we see is that this was right. So do we see where the error was in this process?" Giving us that grace, that we're all sort of working through together. It takes time.

45

M: Yes, yes. I was just about to say – week four. I don't think everything has been set up yet, in terms of the students being totally okay with showing all their work or explaining everything. But week 10, week eight, they know through what you've said and what you've done, that they buy in to your grace, and then it starts going with everything else.

What you said about, the non-verbals, you could be like, you could be having professional development and you could be told, "Hey, you should have grace. You should tell them they're not wrong." And then you could have somebody who's saying, "you're not wrong," but in a condescending way with the non-verbals. I really appreciate the neutrality in your response in order to try to foster their own self-evaluation, their own independence when it comes to all this. So that it's not just that they look at you as the authority in everything. In that scenario, it's all *dependence*. You're the independent variable. They're the dependent variable. And so they're looking at you like, "am I right? Am I right?" They look straight at you. How I handle that is that I either move myself physically to the back, or I just try to figure something else out, like, "whoa, what do you all think?" And even the neutrality, it's hard at first. Yeah. It's very, very hard. They've been kind of preconditioned to think that knowledge is from the teacher. So once they feel a little bit of that confidence that they can evaluate? What else can they do?

And she never thought she would get to that space. But I knew she would because I know what she's got inside of her.

C: Yeah, and that's actually a really important skill for them to see. Because one of the hardest parts, I think, when you are supporting a student in, let's say, office hours. They're like, "what about this? Is this right?" And then they do a step in there, "Is this right?" The confirmation that they needed every step is coming from the sort of erasure of their ability to see what's next, and to have confidence in themselves that they can do it. I'm very lucky that the work that I've put into now at the stage that I'm at with my office hours, sometimes what I'll say is, "Okay, would you like to finish this problem together?" They will say "No. I can see what's next. I'm going to finish this and I'll be okay." Or "Yes, please, can we finish this step-by-step? Can you go back and show me?" Which is fine, right!? Because I can still do that. And so what ends up happening is that you are providing a space for students to gain confidence in themselves. I had a student in my last office hour figure out a problem on her own. And she said, "this is the first time I've done a problem like this by myself. And I'm going to go tell my friends." She was so proud of herself, and I said, "I'm so proud of you. I'm so happy for you. You've done it." And she never thought she would get to that space. But I knew she would, right, because I know what she's got inside of her. And if I support her in this way, without taking over and just be like, "let me just do it for you." But give her the space or provide the space for her to gain this confidence so that she could do it. She would get there.

M: Yes, providing opportunities. I always feel like it's co-creating the space, because they're part of that, right? I think it's extremely tough. Yeah. And I think that there are some times and I know, I was like this, where I'd be like "Oh, I provided this amount of space, or whatever it was, and you didn't take it. So maybe I shouldn't provide it in the future". And so now, instead of like me keeping on with grace, I go the opposite way, just because of an instance.

C: I mean, I think we sometimes really think all of our students are going to be exactly the same. And that we figured this out, we have figured this teaching thing out. And that's the thing with radical grace — we will talk about this in a later chapter — *it's not check boxes, it is a mindset*. So going into a space and being like, "I used to do this for my students, but no one would take advantage of it. So I'm not going to do it anymore." Well, those students maybe didn't need it, or didn't feel comfortable doing it. But you've changed who you are and you're more inviting and you're now providing radical grace and more students are having a positive experience. So taking away your grace because people weren't using it is so weird to me. "Well, you weren't using my grace. So now you don't get it anymore. The next people have now learn there is no grace. You've ruined it for everyone", that sort of thing. It's so weird to punish the group because you felt slighted.

M: And future groups, too, right? And for what?

C: I think it's very different to say, I used to be able to do this, my situation has changed, and I cannot do this.

M: Yes. I can't do the five minute oral exams for 50 students anymore.

C: Right. My situation has changed. You may have heard that this used to be a thing that I did. Let me explain to you why I don't do that anymore.

M: It's funny that there are certain times where I take a step just slightly back in my classroom. And I make explicit the little micro-movement, the micro-grace that occurred. And I just go, "Hey, look, this is why I approached it this way. This is why I didn't say anything this way. Right? Because I want to foster your own confidence – your own approaches. Your own understanding is so amazing." I'm making those little movements explicit, not all the time, because then we will be in the meta almost all the time. But I'm making it explicit every once in a while just to make sure that they know that I'm not answering not out of malice or frustration with them or removing myself, but rather giving them a little bit of time to go over it, giving others a little bit of time and so forth.

It's interesting, now that I think about it, I have a part of my exam that I do recently, where I say that I made a mistake on this problem. And I asked them, not only to point out the mistake, the content, but also give me feedback in the way that you would think would help me improve. And they are responding with "Oh, you did so well, with a lot of these things." Because I'm valuing their approaches in the classroom, they are noticing and valuing my sample approach. I think that's a big deal. Right? That little grace – now you can see it in group work. Now you can see it when they're with their friends or at home, you know? Some have siblings that they go and talk to them about math, right? That's, it's just, it's those little things that can make a huge difference and have a butterfly effect.

C: I mean, it totally does. Because I can see the impact when micrograce doesn't happen. I don't always have the opportunity to have conversations with my graders about how they write comments on my students papers. And so sometimes my students will come to me, and they will talk to me about the wording or they'll talk to each other like, "wow, this is really mean the way this person said this" and "I don't understand why the person wrote that". So it doesn't match with how we speak to each other in the classroom. They get this feedback, and it's not given with grace sometimes. I'm not saying they should write "Oh, you are completely wrong but you tried. Plus four out of five." But there are ways to say to people, "you know, you did a really great job here, here are some of the spaces where you need some improvement." I think everyone is expecting to get feedback for improvement, and I think it's the way we give that feedback that matters. And of course, not everyone speaks the same. We don't all have that soft tone, or that soft writing tone. But there are ways that we can change out certain words to be read in a way that is helpful to them versus "this person hates my guts." For some reason, with the students, it's either-or.

M: But because of the default, that changing of tone is *radical*. Even if you were neutral in your comments, it's going to be taken as harsh. I thought for a long time that I'd be very harsh at the beginning and then I would recede. But what is that going to do?

C: Right? I mean, think about that, like, okay, so think about if that's what you did with children. It just confuses them, and it causes mistrust; it's *gaslighting*. If you're just like, "No, you can't have cookies before dinner" and then the next day you give them cookies before dinner. Let's just put it there. This like, "No, you don't get more time to do this. How dare you even think you can?" And then later in the course you switch up. "Why didn't you just ask for more time? Of course you can have it!" Who wants to be in that kind of relationship, that kind of situation where the person is just back and forth. You don't know where you stand, and it just feels weird. Especially if in the end, you're going to relax those things, just relax them at the beginning. Just relax. Yeah, and if you're not, that's fine. But maybe try to say: "This is a rule for a reason. What I have experienced in the past is this. Here are some ways that I have provided grace. In case things need to change for you as an individual we can discuss, but as a group, this is the sort of structure we have." We have all thought about those rules, that structure, for likely multiple reasons. I'm not saying like get rid of all of your structure, but have some grace when you're creating and enforcing it. And don't do this back and forth action. It's confusing and it's probably really harmful for anyone involved.

We detailed interactions within the classroom because those reactions from us as instructors can make a big difference in the environment of the classroom. These are the ripples that turn into waves. It can be a reaction about process instead of certainty, or excitement about their contribution, or even the non-verbal positioning of yourself within the physical space of the class. All can be pieces of radical grace that add up.

Chapter VIII

What if They take Advantage?

WHEN WE DISCUSS RADICAL GRACE, we are often asked this question: "What do you do if a student takes advantage of you?" We always have a difficult time answering this question, so we discussed why this is a tough question for us to answer.

M: I think the hardest thing for others is trying to incorporate radical grace in their lives. What do you think are some of the difficulties or challenges of that? Perhaps not only in mathematics teaching but in any capacity?

C: So... the push-back I often get from folks is "but what do you do if they take advantage of you?" And I think the idea that's missing there is trust. And the fact that if you're giving grace then... I don't know it feels weird to say someone's taking advantage of you, because I think anytime people feel taken advantage of – if a student lies about something then there's something else going on. I think it's important to think that way when you have a relationship.

That's the thing: radical grace comes with a relationship. It's not just like this thing I just let them do whatever they want. You have a real relationship with them so that you trust them and they trust you, or at the very least you're working towards gaining their trust. They feel comfortable asking you for what they need as opposed to just like doing these things. And there's a sense that, because you care, they want to do what they can in that time or do their best with what they have, and that they are comfortable asking when they feel like they need something.

So this idea of "you're going to be taken advantage of", is so weird to me because… Listen, if a student takes more time to do all the assignments and they're "taking advantage of my radical grace", then there's something happening there. That student needs that, or they think they need it. You know they either need it, or they think they need it, but those are equal to me, so who cares? Let them have it. Who loses?

When we all feel like we're supported and can do our best with support, what's wrong with that?

When we all feel like we're supported and can do our best with support, what's wrong with that? It's so bizarre to me that people just don't want to do that. Other people may think it is not fair that you're giving everyone that same opportunity if they need it or not. Fair? What is fair really? It's more equitable this way. Because I have a variety of things that I can provide for you as an individual. Use what you need – it is yours. And if someone doesn't need it, someone doesn't use what I can provide, it's not hurting them that someone else used it.

M: But that's a conscious effort. Like equal and fair, and all this other stuff that really undermines a lot of the diversity and disparity. You're telling me that students coming into my class have an equal understanding of all the stuff that happened prior? It's not true. You know, especially in calculus out of all places where there's huge disparity. So if I take 15 minutes to explain this to one student... So two things: 1) competitiveness. It's not fair, right, because I'm competing, and 2) authority. The whole definition of authority, or power if you will in a general sense, but like this notion of like taking advantage of authority. I control what I can control, and that involves providing opportunities. Whatever the students do with it, it's theirs. But I can only control what I can control. Taking advantage – that's on them. And you know what if they do, they've got to sit with that. They've got to "eat" that themselves and think about that.

Back on this one thing – I'd rather err on the side of talking with everybody here right, so that a few the students can be like, "oh yeah, well, he does actually care." Consider the opposite – shutting down everybody because they're taking advantage. It's a deficit viewpoint to only look at students taking advantage.

C: You know it reminded me of like there's some things in the world that were created for specific people. Like handicapped buttons on doors. But we all can use them. Is it taking advantage if I use it? The idea that a student is using an opportunity just to ease some stress. Sure, they could have done it in this set amount of time and stress themselves out for that stuff. It's just the idea of taking advantage is so weird to me, because I don't know the scenario where that happens.

> *It's a deficit viewpoint to only look at students taking advantage.*

M: Again, going back to it, the authoritative or a competitive state where you're taking advantage of the three points that I'm giving you, whereas, in one of my classes, they took a quiz. They didn't do so well. I can have you redo it and learn from it. And to me it's not about points; it's about, "are you learning from these exercises, activities, and so forth.

And if you're not, then we got to figure out another way. All I want you to do is try to understand."

And don't get me wrong, I think I went through a school system that was very extrinsically motivated. So I understand how hard it is to unlearn. And to focus on learning. Not just learning, but learning first, and then grades come after that. Maybe we can incorporate some extrinsic motivation opportunities that can meld into intrinsic motivation. But if I can give them a chance to learn more, isn't that the goal at the end of the day? I hear from so many people like, "oh, I took this class and then I just forgot all of it." I don't want that. If anything, you can forget all of it as long as you have the confidence that you could open up a book or go on Wikipedia and, within a couple minutes, relearn it.

C: I think there's a shift – it's not that we don't want them to learn. We want them to think. And the idea that we're teaching rote memorization will be lost when they don't *use* it. Right now I'm teaching calculus. I'm teaching integrals, and I don't freaking remember all the solutions to certain integrals. I don't. But you know what I remember are the rules, because I understand where they come from. So I did not remember the anti-derivative of secant. What I did is I tried some things, the first thing I tried didn't work, and I could see that it wasn't going to work. I didn't just keep going, because I was like "well, this has to be it, and there's no other way to do anything." So I have the ability to think about a problem and logically figure out what works and what doesn't work. But do I remember how to do everything, the first time I see it? No. I have song lyrics stuck in my head. I don't have these answers to these problems, I have more important things in there. But what I did learn how to do is think and figure out how to solve a question, and that's what I want them to be able to do – solve and ask questions.

M: Similar notion, I do want to add two more things that I have. One is confidence that I can approach the problem and even persevere, which is something that I have to discuss sometimes in class. And two… and

I cannot stress this enough, my life is very privileged. And that allows me to have a lot of clear working memory. And therefore I can just sit down and concentrate on this problem. It's not the same as one of my calculus students, because they have all these other things that may be going on in their lives that are impacting them.

It's not to say that I don't have things that are impacting me. Right? But I do have the mental capacity, at least in the working memory, that's cleared because of some of the things that I'm afforded in society coupled with some of the things that I'm afforded mathematically. So I just want to, I want to add that those are huge.

And it goes back to anxiety. When you're anxious, three or four out of the five of your mental chunks are taken over by a cloud. So to give two extra days for a student to do an assignment. I have a take-home test and an in-class test. To allow them to concentrate on the take-home stuff, it costs me little. And it gives them that kind of support.

C: Yeah, we are definitely out of the space where we don't have to be on the edge every moment. Any moment where I've got to prove or show or do this thing – we're not at that stage any longer. So, I think it's very important to remember that our students aren't at that yet. We need to check our privilege on that axis.

But I just talked about this with a student recently. You get to this sort of stage where you forget what it was like before you got there. And we were discussing moving tax brackets. Moving from being a graduate student, making graduate student money, or a postdoc, or you know first couple jobs, and then we're at this later stage where we're assistant professors, associate professors. We sometimes forget what the impact of a bill for $150 was, right!? Like that would have had a huge impact on me as a graduate student for sure. And now that I am at a different stage, you know, I can see that bill and I'll pay it. This is a lot of money to ask from someone who doesn't have steady income. Someone who has a higher debt to income ratio. You forget. I forget. Because I've been in that situation before and I had forgotten.

I think that is what we do to our students sometimes. We forget what it's like to be a student. An undergraduate student, graduate student – all the stress. The different classes they are balancing, the life they are balancing. And we often just think about them being in the space with us. I say to my students all the time, "I know that you are a full person. A full human being in this world. You didn't just show up in this class space for me and then you're going to dissipate when I leave. I know you have a full life, so please just let me know what you need it's yours. Because you have all this other stuff going on and it's easy for me to forget that you have other stuff going on, or to think that the other stuff you have going on is less important but that's not fair. To me, that's your life, not my life, that's your life.

That's what I think happens is that we forget about that, but what helps me are these reflections. I asked my students and I listened to them, because I can understand what's happening second-hand now. It's not first-hand for me anymore. I forgotten what it's like. If I really tried to think about the stress, I can't even imagine because it's been too long. But they can tell me how they feel, and I can listen to them, and base my ideas about the class on what they're saying, because they're living it. And I think that's what's missing from some people, this idea of radical grace, they're just like, "but they're going to take advantage of me," and it's like "who cares? You're at the privilege spot here!"

M: What does that even mean that they took advantage of you?

C: You shifted some power their way? It's so bizarre. It does come down to competition and to ego, I think. "I did all these things, and they did this to me." So, they needed more, and they didn't know they could ask you for it, but you can adjust later. "I wish I had known that you needed this. This is something I can offer in the future." All of this is a learning process and what happens, I think, is it goes the opposite way.

Instructors can just think "I *used* to do [insert helpful thing], and then I saw that students were taking more of [helpful thing], so I stopped offering [helpful thing]." I always want to say "that's the way you went with it?! You saw this happening and that was your feedback? You're looking at this data all wrong or just adding more hoops."

M: You know, like more pitfalls and the "gotchas." "I'm going to catch them in the act of cheating," or whatever it is. But it's so wild how pervasive it is. I'll give you an example, one of my students today in class was like, "I need to go to the restroom. I put all of my devices on the table. Can I go?" He preemptively thought that I would not let him go to the bathroom without putting all the devices table. I didn't know what to do other than say "yeah, go." But I couldn't believe what was happening, in my mind. It was just like, "this is the norm." The norm is, "I already expect you to cheat." I mean, in his defense, it might have been just, "I don't want to even have the question of it." So it may not have been a reflection on me. But still.

C: It's trained behavior because they've been in classes where that's what happened, I mean they've probably been in classes, where the instructors like, "no one can go to the bathroom during this time."

M: I can't even fathom this. There it is right there. It's psychological where it's like this is how much I trust and value you. If you do that, you're going to get a reciprocation, and then it's going to become a radical grace space or it will become adversarial.

The idea of students "taking advantage" of our grace comes from the adversarial relationship that is very common in the classroom. We cannot trust the students to know what they need and to ask for it. Because the foundation of radical grace is trust in our students and seeing them as whole people, we do not make assumptions about what they need, we provide what we can. This important distinction allows for everyone to feel less stress. It also reminds us that every identity is deserving of grace, no matter what perceived privilege they come into the classroom with.

CHAPTER IX

ACCESS TO REST

Candice Price

WHEN I WAS ASSISTANT-COACHING COLLEGE-LEVEL rugby, I learned so many lessons about teaching. One learning opportunity comes to my mind often. One team I was supporting had many great players, but one stood out above the others. This exceptional player, whom I will call E.P., was phenomenal. Rugby is a very tough, collision sport. I often describe it as a mix between football and soccer, with the collisions of football and stop-less play of soccer. It can be played in two ways: 15s and 7s. In 15s, each team has 15 players on the field at a time and the game consists of two 40-minute halves played on a 100-meter field (called the pitch). In 7s, there are 7 players from each team, playing on the same size pitch with 7-minute halves. Either game is exhausting to play, each for unique reasons as you can imagine.

E.P. was absolutely amazing at both versions of rugby, but especially at 7s. The amount of energy she showed on the pitch made many of us feel that she was unstoppable. But, at one point during a 7s tournament, I looked over at E.P. and realized she had played about 5 full games that day alone. This is a lot to ask one person. It felt to me as if we had made her responsible for the team's success. This is not rugby culture. The game of rugby utilizes every body type, and every person on the team is important. This creates a beautiful game that heavily relies on teamwork. But, we had created an environment that I feared put a lot of pressure on this one player to be excellent always. We had perhaps made her feel that she could not ask for rest.

I looked over to the head coach and said "Maybe we should sit E.P. the next game?" He gave me a questioning look and said "Why?" "Well she has played every game so far and she might be tired." He then looked at me and said, "That's the thing with E.P., she doesn't get tired." But everyone gets tired. Everyone. And we all deserve to rest. No matter what.

Sometimes grace looks like rest. It looks like rest even when we think we don't deserve it, when we think it needs to be earned. I have often been shocked when my students that are perceived as the strongest, stumble or struggle. Why? Because I made assumptions about them. I made assumptions that they would not need my support, that they have it all under control.

> *But everyone gets tired. Everyone. And we all deserve to rest. No matter what.*

But what if I assume that everyone needs support at some point in time and I encourage all of my students by letting them know they have support at any time? What if I check in on all of my students, not just when they struggle? I can create opportunities for them to share with me how they are doing by creating an environment where they feel like I am listening to them and I care about them. Sometimes grace looks like care. Sometimes grace looks like the opportunity to share who you are as a whole person, not just a person in this classroom space with me. What changes if I create a space where students are "allowed" to rest?

Where they don't have to fear showing weakness or struggle? Where struggle and rest are a celebrated part of the journey? I believe when I do this, it creates a place where my students feel comfortable being vulnerable, trying new things, taking chances, resting when they need to, to take care of themselves and each other. This is one way that I can foster community in my classroom. A space where students like E.P. don't have to hide that they need to rest, to hide that they are tired. And it is a space where we all recognize this need. A space where we all provide and are provided access to rest and support… without being asked.

Chapter X

What is the Formula for Radical Grace?

Another thing that often happens when we talk about radical grace is that those in the audience ask us what to do and how to do it. The specifics of radical grace looks differently for different people and courses. But, radical grace is a teaching philosophy, not a pedagogy. In this conversation, we candidly discuss the difference.

C: There are people who will say, "I've not gotten any complaints, so why should I change?" And I think that that is such a such a striking statement. Because I think we think about complaints, and particularly one-way complaints, as "well if no one has ever said anything to me about what I am doing, then I don't have to change." Or if someone has said something then I can just brushed it off because "they don't understand".

And I think that's very telling if someone is saying to you that this method isn't working. And you're just like, "well you just don't understand the method." It is on you to be a bit more transparent about why you've made these decisions, and to have a discussion with the person about what the benefits are of this decision you've made. Of course, I get that people are like, "why should I have to explain myself?!" Well, we're talking about students who are adults. We should speak to them as adults.

We are talking to people who want to learn from us. And instead of shutting them down by saying "I don't have to tell you why I'm doing what I'm doing", if we have these open conversations with them, it really opens the door to them learning. If we care about that part, then we will care about opening that door... we will care about transparency.

And there are some people that have never heard any negative feedback. But have you felt it? What are your students feeling like in that space? Have you given them the opportunity to even tell you how they feel in that space? Are students coming back to your classes? Are students recommending your classes to other people, or are they just saying "that class is fine?" And is that what you want? That might be what you want, and that's fine. But that is just not what I want. I want my students to leave having a positive experience, not just a neutral one. Because neutral adds nothing to their experience. I want my students to leave understanding why I teach the way that I teach. I want my students to feel like they had power in that space and that I want to share this power with them as much as possible. I want them to feel like they had ownership of the material... ownership of the conversation... ownership of the course. Because once I have that buy-in, then they have ownership of their learning and that's my goal.

So the question is: What's your goal?

M: It's interesting to me because I feel like I get more complaints about my teaching *because* there is more of an open environment. Because there's more grace. Because I want to know what they're thinking. And I think someone who says "I haven't gotten complaints at all" is probably because there's an environment that shuts down all of those. I don't even feel like I can go to that instructor...at all.

C: Right!? "The comments have been disabled on this video".

M: Yes! Great metaphor. So the other thing I think about when you said, "explaining": Don't we do this in academia? When we're creating some research or creative activity, aren't we justifying it as well?

C: We should be.

M: Shouldn't the same happen for teaching activities? And it all boils down to "what's the norm?" I get push-back because I'm going against the norm. Me going against the norm is probably for the benefit of the students. So you haven't had a complaint in so many years, probably because the norm is that you do what you do. And that's it.

C: And everyone just knows that's what you're gonna do.

M: That's the handshake agreement. "You come in, student, you sit down, and you listen to me. You leave and then that's it. You listen to me." It's just so wild and frustrating.

It makes me even more aware of radical grace, because I think a lot about not only where what I did, and how that shaped me, but what grace has been provided, and what hasn't been, in my life. And what I can do to change that and make that better. There was a motto throughout my life. I don't know who said it, one of my parents, that said, "let's make this thing better than what we came to it." How can I do that in every aspect of my life? And one of those aspects is in my teaching. I have to address people who may not like our book. Why is teaching and your research or creative activity siloed? Why can't either of these coexist and play with each other? For example, I believe,

Why is teaching and your research or creative activity siloed? Why can't either of these coexist and play with each other?

part of large aspects of my teaching are kind of having students research and play and try to figure out things like I would in my research. I've been very excited to hear multiple people that I've talked to give their students challenging problems or problems that they don't even know what the answers are, and let students play and and give them a space or a playground, if you will. To go ahead and just play around. Why is there a separation between the two?

C: The learning is play! I think we've decided at some point that you cannot be playing and learning at the same time and it's a very interesting thing because it starts quite young. I think about kindergartners really just having a good time learning, learning how to count, because they're playing these games, maybe in first grade. And then all of a sudden it's like, "sit in your desk, listen to me, write on this paper," and that's such a shift that we've done. It really does, I think, drive out a lot of creativity. It's just a vibe for sure.

You should be leaving discomfort and moving into more discomfort... But remember when moving into discomfort, you're moving into a space where there's a learning curve.

You know, one thing I was going to say is that there are people where this work isn't comfortable. The thing is, anytime you transition it's not going to be comfortable. There's gotta be some discomfort. And, in fact, you should be leaving discomfort and moving into *more* discomfort. One reason that people often leave discomfort is it just didn't work for them. They tried something and it didn't work. But remember when moving into discomfort, you're moving into a space where there's a learning curve.

And that's going to be uncomfortable because there are going to be mistakes made, things that will be hard, and it's so easy to slide back into the discomfort that you know. Because there's comfort in the discomfort that you know. Right?! "This is safe, I don't feel comfortable with it, but it's safe because I'm not taking any risks and I don't understand the discomfort, and if I adjust…"

I get that there's so many things in our lives that we have a hard time letting go of. We have a hard time changing because of the fear that can come with change. But I just want to think about all the benefits that come with that discomfort of change. The benefit of adding more weights to the barbell. The benefit of pushing to run the extra mile. The benefit of doing these things to improve. Things that are hard at first, but then become easier the more we do it. It may never be easy, but hopefully it will become more comfortable as time passes. Helping me not slide back into the comfortable discomfort that I was so familiar with before.

M: This goes hand-in-hand, but non-routine-ness and flexibility are a huge aspect of any part of life. I can't even imagine someone who is 90 years old right now, and has gone through the great depression to now, and just goes and sees all of the technological advances. They have to either understand it or completely avoid it. And I feel the same way with teaching.

We have students here who have to handle 21st-century ideas, difficulties, and notions. There was an article that said that 33% of college graduates are going into a field that has not yet been made. Thinking about radical grace involves knowing not only the instructor, but the students have to get into discomfort because of the non-routine. I think routine and comfort go hand-in-hand.

But it's also going back to your discussion about making it easier, because you're also being more flexible. You're stretching yourself metaphorically. With that stress and stretch causes pain or difficulty.

But it also causes more flexibility in your life. Radical grace, I think, is the approach to handling a lot of the affective issues that stem from non-routine-ness. That stem from us having difficult situations in our life that we're not expecting. As people have some power in our classrooms, can we approach those flexible places, not with hardness or coldness, but with a warmth, help, and support. That's what I feel like this book is all about. It's aspects of our lives that guided us to caring, to wanting people to do well, and that's radical, right?

C: It really is an affectionate story about teaching and how we got to this place of having radical grace in the classroom, and showing our appreciation and affection for what teaching could be.

> *Radical grace, I think, is the approach to handling a lot of the affective issues that stem from non-routine-ness.*

M: Because it's got to be better than this.

C: Right!? It's got to be better than what we've experienced.

M: We can make things better than what they were before. Thank you.

C: Thank you!

It is important for us to say that there is not one way to have radical grace in the classroom. We do not have a step by step resource on how to make the classroom space exactly like ours. We wouldn't want that. What fits our classroom, our students, varies even between semesters. The goal is to start with trust and an understanding of our students as whole people. With this as the root, radical grace becomes the fruit. There is no one way to have radical grace, but it doesn't exist with out those two things.

CHAPTER XI

DOES BALANCE IMPLY CHANGE?

BALANCE IS A BIG ISSUE IN MANY ACADEMIC CAREERS. Figuring out where to put energy and time so that you are not drained is a challenge. While much of this conversation centers around balance in the classroom, some of these aspects can translate into other aspects of an academic career. Classrooms, students, and lives are not fixed, so change is always present. How can we think about changing balance so that radical grace is maximized?

C: So I think we probably need to have a discussion about balance, right? And the multiple ways that we see balance when talking about radical grace. And perhaps the first balance conversation needs to be about balancing the grace we're giving ourselves and the grace we're providing to students or what that has to look like for the whole space to be a radical-grace space.

M: The toughest conversation perhaps of the whole book. Because I will say, I don't know, and I will never know. It's a maximization problem, to me, to try to figure out that balance. We get comments all the time about, "but I have 200 students, right? How can I handle this?" And on one hand, we're not giving any recipes for radical grace, no check-boxes. But on the other hand, if you believe in it, then it should permeate. And we've said that before. And so I guess finding that balance involves kind of giving yourself some grace to kind of tinker with what goes on in the classroom, how you're handling it, and what you have energy and capability to do. But it's tough. That balance kind of shifts for me personally, daily. Sometimes I can provide a bit more, or come into the classroom with a bit more, sometimes not at all. And we've talked about this as well, with grace with others. There's some times where students kind of recognize that and feel that and they give grace back. That's when you know you've made it in some sense.

How do you handle the balance?

What needs to shift in order for radical grace to be happening right now, not just for my students, and not just for me, but for for both of us together?

C: I mean, I'm in the same boat, as you – I don't know. But I think that you've said something really important here: it does change. It changes every day, maybe. But it also changes and it depends on the person. It depends on who's practicing radical grace. It looks different for different classes, it looks different for different individuals. And I think that's an important thing that, you know, the conversation we're having in this book, in this podcast, isn't like, "this is how you do radical grace." But the idea is, "here's the philosophy, what does it look like for you? What does it look like for your class?" And, you know, I dare to say that this idea you're saying that the balance shifts is this idea of a fulcrum. Like, where do you place the fulcrum to have that balance? That center-of-mass question, because, you know, the weight shifts, right? How much do my students need right now? How much do I need right now? And how do I balance that? Where do I place my fulcrum for this? And I think that is a question I asked myself every day or every week, even, maybe not every day. But how is this week going? How is this moment going? Right? What can I show? Where do I need to place the fulcrum right now? What needs to shift in order for radical grace to be happening right now, not just for my students, and not just for me, but for both of us together? It's this combination I have to think about.

M: I have this difficulty as well. Why is it hard to think of things in terms of a spectrum? Instead of the ends?

C: I think it's because we've been forced to think about this idea as a binary, as "either-or"? And I think this has been said and made explicit a few times to us in different ways. But this idea of "either-or" is a characteristic of white supremacy culture. There's this idea of "you have this or you have that", there's no in between, there is no "and". When we could be thinking about it as a spectrum, right? We're thinking about it as if we have the numbers zero and one versus the interval, or all of the numbers from zero to one, including a half, a fourth, and so on. And so I think that's the way we have to sort of shift our mindset. To think more about this spectrum and that we all can fall in the these different spots in the spectrum of radical grace, different spots, different days, different semesters, different all of that, and be okay with that.

M: Yeah. I also feel like it's easier to say things are this or that. I can always go, "Oh, I'm this or not this," and then that's it. There is no other discussion about it. Whereas with a spectrum, you've got to think a little bit deeper about where you are at. And if you can think of scenarios such as, "if I do this 5% more, what is that outcome going to do? Or 5% less, and how that's going to shift things?" And that's tough, because the spectrum means that you've got to move it in any different place, right? Not just all or nothing, right? It's not a light switch. It's a dimmer.

C: Ooh, I like that. It's a dimmer. I totally agree. And I think we're sort of stuck in this categorization of people and things like good student, bad student, A student, B, student, C student, D student. I will just say, that's always been so weird to me to say, "oh, but that is a C student." And I'm like, "in what way? So in your class, they got a C, is that what you're saying to me? But in my class, they got an A." So you're viewing them as one thing, and I get to view them as a whole person that can be a variety of things, right? No one is just one thing. I love this dimmer idea.

M: This reminds me a lot of 10 years ago in my life, in a professional development conference, there was this concept that was brought up of "freezing" people. And I think that it's a big deal. When I say that some student is a C student, that means that I'm freezing them in this C student moment. Whereas I think a graceful approach to that would be to say, this is a student who, you know, across 16 weeks can fluctuate all over the place and needs balance, needs that fulcrum shift at certain times.

C: Just changing, I think, our perspective of students in that way can just revolutionize our classroom spaces instead of seeing our students frozen in time. "I had this student last semester, they were like this. This is the student that I know." And I'm not saying delete data, but I'm saying don't act like the data is the whole picture of a person. And think about, "New Year, New Me," right? We say this all the time. I think that it's important. I think we want to think of everyone as improving. Everyone has to change, right? Life is changing. Everyone is improving,

A graceful approach to that would be to say, this is a student who, you know, across 16 weeks can fluctuate all over the place and needs balance.

everyone is changing. And we wouldn't want someone to look at us and think of us frozen in time. We would want to be given this grace that we are adaptable. We are learning, we are reflecting. Why wouldn't we want to see the same thing in our students, or just assume the same thing about our students?

M: That's precisely the thing I was thinking about. This balance notion extends not only between teacher and student, but between oneself and how much grace you can provide in that certain scenario with *yourself*. How much work and life-balance happens, and giving yourself the grace at home to go, "Okay, I just need to drop this right now." That is super hard. I'm not saying that it's easy at all. I have a very difficult time with that, with worrying about deadlines, worrying about this, worrying about that. But over the years, as I've given myself some grace in those moments, they kind of gnaw at me less.

C: And I like that this has to be balanced because you can't just drop everything always. Because you still want to balance in the way that you're not just providing yourself grace but also grace to your students. And that does sometimes look like providing feedback. Letting them know you're there to support them and here's the ways of support. Here is some feedback. Here's some information about how are you doing in that class. And I know that it can sometimes be very difficult for us to find the time to do that. But there are moments where we have to shift that fulcrum so that the balance isn't just, "we are getting all the benefit, and our students are getting none."

M: We don't want to be frozen ourselves And I was thinking about this. People label students as C students. Have we been labeled as C teachers?

C: Listen – I'm sure. I mean, we see this in like, the Rate My Professors, like the stagnant-ness, (yes, that can be a word) of our student evaluations that we have to keep over the years. It's like, "oh, here's your student evaluations from year one of teaching." But I'm a different person. And hopefully, yes hopefully, in year 2, 3, 4, and 5. So can we look at longevity? Can we look at the change? Versus "well, in year one, someone said this about you. Let's hold on to this one thing." Do you see that theme throughout, and is it a positive thing? Yeah, even if it's positive, are we improving on that? Are we stagnant? Are we sort of stuck and frozen in that time?

M: So then, does balance imply change?

C: It's got to. Because I think what's happening is that some sort of viewing this as a teeter totter. Some folks may say this apparatus a *seesaw*, but I am from the West Coast so I say *teeter totter*, but whatever... Anyhow, I'm envisioning putting weight, more weight on different size sides of this teeter totter. So, of course, there's a change. But once I start adding weight or taking off weight, I've got to move the fulcrum for balance. It has got to shift. So there's all of this change happening, right? Things are changing with respect to other things, other pieces. And so it is a constant change that's happening, maybe, explicitly, maybe implicitly, maybe just in the back of our minds, we're shifting. In the very moment, we're shifting. But yes, I think it has balance has to be changed.

Does balance imply change? It's got to.

M: I was thinking to myself, does radical grace to yourself mean that you're lifting the weights off of that teeter totter?

C: As opposed to adding? Yeah. Wow...

M: And, and not only that, like, we talked about the little moments of radical grace, right? Is having a belief of radical grace, meaning that you're actually removing some of those difficulties you have in those little moments too?

C: You know, it's very interesting. I think we're thinking about weight as a negative. Right? So adding weight to the teeter totter is a negative. So yes, I think radical grace would be removing that weight. But if we shifted the mindset and thought about grace itself as the teeter totter, right? And are there moments where there's more grace being given in a space, and so we have to shift the fulcrum to even out? Or is the fulcrum grace? We may need to work this metaphor out more.

M: I do think now, if the teeter totter was grace, that there might be this zero-sum game that's going on. And so I was thinking some 3D thing, but I think because it's true, like you can, you can move some things, you can move some fulcrum, that has an advantage, or I don't know if that's the word for it for many things. It builds many things. That little shift of 5% actually equalled quite a bit in terms of different amounts of what's going on grace-wise for yourself and for others, right. So it may not only be a teeter totter, but a teeter totter that also grows? That expands?

C: Wow. This is quite the metaphor. It's actually really interesting because I think about this metaphor when it comes to equity versus equality, which we talked about. And so if someone has more access, more spaces where they feel comfortable, more privilege in that axis, then they're weighed down even more. They're closer to the ground. To the goal, right? That's equality right down the middle. So equity would mean that you have to shift towards the side that has less access, less support, less privilege, less identity in that space, less power in that space. And so that is equity. Right? That's what equity means is that, it's not going to be in the middle, it can't be equality, because even if we said, "Okay, we're all gonna start at the same spot", we're not bringing the same thing. Yeah. So we can't even if we're starting at the same spot, we're all bringing different things to that space. And so we need to shift in order for us to be able to move forward in the same space. But that's how I think about it, is this shift in the fulcrum versus being right in the middle.

M: It reminds me of the conversation of having like, a collective individual, where you're highlighting each individual's strengths in this collective space. And some may already feel like they can highlight themselves much more than others. And how do we create that space where we're moving. It's like toggling a little like on the soundbar.

C: A little bit of bass, a little bit of treble.

M: Yeah, exactly. But to me, that is all encompassed by kind of this notion that you have to bring in the grace, that it has to be radical, because that environment hasn't even defaulted towards where you can bring yourself.

C: Yeah. Right. And I love this idea of the collective individual, because what you're saying is that each of you are important to the whole, as opposed to each of you are important, period. Or the whole is important. Each of us is important to the whole. So each important and the whole is important, and *together* we make this work.

M: It's bigger. It's creating the blocks, instead of having the blocks around. It's tough. I do want to say that this is a struggle that I've had quite often with balance, balance with everything. But I think again, there's that notion of collective individual, where I go into spaces, and I talk with people about how they handle work-life balance, or how they handle what goes on in the classroom. And then I try to incorporate, but maybe it doesn't work for me. Maybe I needed this or that. And I think one thing that is required is balancing a little bit with time– maybe it's a 2-dimensional board instead of a 1-dimensional seesaw – and providing some time for reflection. Not only for my students, but for myself as well. Because I need to sit back and go, "Wait, what happened here? And how can I tinker with that in order for it to be better – whatever that means for me."

C: Whatever that means for you. I love that. Because what's better for you doesn't necessarily mean it's better for me as an individual, but maybe it's better for the collective. I also really liked that you said, you can try other things, things that other people have done, and maybe it doesn't work. But it is important to *try*. Because you just don't know, I think sometimes we get sort of stuck like "that would never work for me," that sort of fixed mindset, that frozen space. And maybe you do know it won't work for you because you've tried it already. But it's always great to try and to reflect. How do I make this thing work for me? Maybe I throw the whole thing away, it doesn't work at all. Or maybe there are bits or pieces that I saw that work really well for me, work really well for this course, work really well for that. It's not check-boxes, it's individual ideas about utilizing grace in this space. What does it look like for you in this space? Right? And it is hard. You said it's so hard, it is hard, but it feels like it's worth it.

M: Grace, trust. Trust, now I'm listening a bit more to the advice, to the conversations, etc, etc. And so, when I get advice, whether it's solicited or more commonly unsolicited, I then can incorporate that. I wrote this blurb for the MAA FOCUS entitled, "What is math? What is education?" And in it, I defined education as ideas that you could either synthesize or reject, and my students had a problem with defining what either of those were. But at the same time, I think that's what goes on in life. We have all these experiences. And we either like come in and go, "Oh, that's interesting." Right? Or we go, "No, thank you." But there's a balance between those two as well.

C: It's a spectrum. Like gender, it's a spectrum.

M: And why not? Why do we have to go binary?

C: We don't.

M: And, okay, riffing off of this, what does it hurt me at all? How does it hurt at all for me to recognize that gender is not binary?

C: It's very interesting, too. Because there are lots of examples of things that we know are not binary, right? It's not hot or cold. There are so many things. But for this?... We can't shift to that mindset. It brings us back to the idea of "either-or". And we do this with so many things. Even for ourselves. "I'm either good at this, or I'm bad at this." There's no space for the improvement that can happen. There's no, "I'm doing okay. And I can get better."

M: The radical part of all of this is recognizing all of these norms that have been created and pushing at them. And pushing till it breaks, okay. There's some times where that happens, too. And we've created our new norms.

C: And as we push what we are doing is moving that fulcrum!

M: Isn't that beautiful? I love it. Thank you.

C: You know what... thank you.

You may have noticed that when we discuss balance, we use the similar metaphor of a "fulcrum" that we use when discussing equity. This is because we see the life/work balance conversation as an equity conversation. Shifting resources or support to the areas that need it most in the moment is a constant in many of our lives. One difference between this conversation and the conversation about equity is that is is zero-sum. We have limited time and resources when it comes to work life balance. There is this wonderful commencement speech given by Shonda Rhimes, the creator of many wonderful shows included Grey's Anatomy and Bridgerton, at Dartmouth's class of 2014 graduation that starts with: "Shonda, how do you do it all? The answer is this: I don't. Whenever you see me somewhere succeeding in one area of my life, that almost certainly means I am failing in another area of my life."

This is something important that we have to recall: We are toggling resources here and it is inevitable that we will feel like we have to give more in one area and less in another. But that is the nature of balance when it comes to work and life, it is give and take. For all of us.

Chapter XII

Puzzles

Miloš Savić

PICTURE THIS. A 5-YEAR-OLD CHILD is working on a puzzle in front of you. The puzzle is 12 pieces, or 24 pieces, or 30... it doesn't matter. But they're working on it. They are turning the same piece, trying it in on the same side of the other piece. Comfortable and happy with attempting it casually, the child works on another piece for the outside of the puzzle.

You, at your age, are thinking: "THE PIECE IS THERE!! What is going on in their minds? Why can't they turn this piece or why can't they flip this piece or why can't they move these pieces together? Don't they see?" The next move you make will determine whether you give grace to that child.

Puzzle-building is not unlike the learning that students do in our classes. In this metaphor, the puzzle itself is your content, and the process of doing the puzzle is the process of understanding and synthesizing the content. Students are flipping the pieces, getting familiar with your content. They are trying to figure out what piece goes with the other piece, but they are also developing what it means to be a scholar in your field.

Would you yell, curse, or get mad at a child for doing their first few puzzles? Would you demean them for not figuring out the puzzle quickly?

When I think of radical grace, I think of the grace given almost naturally to people. I remember how kind people were when we walked around with babies, or when I was on crutches (reader: these two are separate). Why is that same level of grace given to others? Which brings me back to the puzzle. I was that parent – eyes wide, incredulous because my child could not see the connections. This happened by reflex on almost any exercise early in my parenting life. I will say that I did not jump in at any time still, although my gosh did I want to! Then, one night, I kept reflecting and thinking about what the outcomes would be for jumping in or not. "If I do it completely for them, then they will watch what I'm doing, but what will they learn? If I completely ignore them and walk away from them, what will they learn?"

It's really interesting how this parallels to teaching. If I lecture the whole time, saying everything, they will watch (or maybe not!) what I do, but what will they learn? If I give them challenging

Unsolicited advice is really tough to listen to.

exercises and then not say anything, what will they do or learn? I always try to have a balance that keeps adjusting to what data my students are providing. That data could include their problem solving, questions they are asking, or verbal/non-verbal actions in the moment. Maybe, in the moment, people are really stumped and I think they need to be shown that you can turn the puzzle piece around. Maybe, they just need me to be around if they have any questions.

I think one aspect of my life that I have had to learn (or un-learn, a theme for me) is that unsolicited advice is really tough to listen to. I can give advice on the puzzle piece, but what if my child is not ready to absorb or understand it? Or what if they don't need that advice now - they are concentrated on the puzzle? Or what if they WERE going to do the exact thing you were giving advice about? Instead, when are we giving grace, truly radical grace (because we KNOW it) to our students that are going through the same situation as that child?

I've learned that more students will listen when they WANT to listen. They want to hear what you are saying as the educator when they have built a need, a trust, or a situation that desires your input. For example, when I need to fix my house, and I believe that I can do it, I will go to YouTube and look up how to do it. I am seeking advice for fixing my house. And, conversely, I am more apt to absorb that advice because I am seeking it.

Did your students click on *your* metaphorical YouTube video? Did they seek your thoughts? Or, in other words, were they motivated to listen to your lecture?

Asking questions about content or process is a main indicator that radical grace is within the class.

I want to stress at this point that I have mini-lectures in my class. I also answer questions, albeit after I've asked their ideas. So, I'm not against lecturing. But when have they had the grace in the classroom to ask questions that necessitate a small discussion? When I was doing professional development for teaching assistants, I would observe classes seeking one thing: questions from students. I would look at what kinds of questions, and how many questions were asked in a class. I knew that there are common questions such as "will this be on the test?", but I also know that there are questions about content, understanding, or process that can be incredibly beneficial to the students. And where did that question come from? More often than not, curiosity. But the "norm" in academia is to not ask those questions or be curious.

Asking questions about content or process is a main indicator that radical grace is within the class.

In my experience, many students are fearful of asking a question in class. There is a stigma that is associated with asking questions because of the perception that one is not smart or that one might be showing off. How many times have you had a student say, "this might be a dumb question, but…"? Applying radical grace in your classroom can be a step towards creating an environment where you can ask questions. Because asking a question about process is the same as asking about how to build a puzzle.

Chapter XIII

Is there Scarcity in Grace?

WHETHER WE ARE CONSCIOUS ABOUT IT OR NOT, there seems to be a prevalent theme in classrooms of scarcity. It's this notion of only having "enough" to give, or that if I give something in this way, then I lose in some other way. It goes hand-in-hand with the issues of zero-sum games in the classroom, with trust, and with classrooms serving as adversarial spaces among students or between students and their teacher. We try to unpack all of these concerns in this chapter.

M: Are we always breaking their trust, no matter what we do as teachers? And I'm saying that because of the countless amounts of times that I value struggle still doesn't fully go into what happens at the end with a grade. "I value your struggle, I value all of the process, but you're still going to get a D." Will the "trust" ever *not* be broken?

C: I think, in certain cases, it's not that you aren't valuing the struggle, there are other things that are weighed heavier. That may be where the shift has to come in with the conversation or with our idea of what learning looks like. We can have a student that struggles throughout and just doesn't get it eventually. They're not ready to move past that struggle – they still need more time. But you see that they're trying, but they just need more time. Do you say, "I see how hard you're working, and if it was based on that, you deserve an A. But that means that you're ready to go to the next step, and you're actually not ready to go to the next step. You still need more time working through this". I think that is one of the hardest parts. Because I've had students who are working really hard, but there is something missing – there's a piece from the past that they don't have, and the connections are just not there. They are trying to build this bridge and there's just not enough material. So they need more time to understand the material and we have a system where we think, "Oh, you have this much time to learn this material and that's all we can give you." So I think that is the issue here. It's like you have to have that kind of conversation with them: "I truly value how hard you're working in this class." I actually have this conversation with students all the time.

I remember one student discussed the idea of enrolling in a calculus two course at the same time as taking calculus one. I said, "you know, I know you're going to work hard. You're gonna work as hard as you can, but what you're signing up for is trying to run a marathon but you have a broken leg. You're going to want to run as hard as you can, but you may not be successful. Because you're trying to do something on an injury, you're going to hurt yourself, maybe even more. So give yourself the time to heal before running this marathon. I don't think you can't do it. I don't think you don't have the ability to work as hard as possible, but why do that to yourself when you can set yourself up for success? You've got to build up to being ready for something like that, so I think that is the conversation to have with a student: " I know you're going to work really hard but do you have all the equipment you *need* to do this?" You could even use like a soccer analogy – you're the goalie but you're trying to play without anybody else on the field. It's just you trying to go block this goal.

M: Right, or even blocking the goal but there's two soccer balls going on at the same time. I think that is kind of the difficulty with that. Well, first of all, that's just tough, period. Building a second floor without having the first floor there. At the same time, I think that the perception in many students' minds is that education is, "let me check off all the boxes. And I know what the game is, and I can probably play that game with both of these classes." But it would be just to check it off. It would not be for a deep understanding of what's going on with the content. It's how I played my undergraduate education. And I think that is the difficult thing that I have with that scenario: You never know when things are going to click and you're going to understand things so much deeper than you would on this surface level. Some students who want to get done and graduate, I know I wanted to get done in three years. But at the same time, I think it's the words "getting done" that's really kind of reverberating in my mind. It brings me back to like definitions of education. What do I want my students to get out of an education? Because persistence is one aspect, but also connection making and deep understanding – thinking deeply about certain topics and making those shifts in thought.

I think when I asked "will we always break their trust?", to me a big thing to think about in teaching, and in life if I may be so grand, is that a lot of things that we think about or say are "for all" statements, and there will always be a situation where we break their trust. I think even grace has this maximum that you're trying to reach but we'll never get to. It is more of an asymptote. You may slip somewhere or have difficulty somewhere, and so I need to keep thinking like it's not an everything or nothing situation. It's not a binary situation, like we have said so many times, but rather a, "how can I figure out ways that maximize my grace, maximize my own health, maximize the content?" There are certain constraints that I'm always toggling in my mind. Not to say that everything's a zero-sum game, but at the same time, where are the ways that I can push a little bit here or there, now that I know what the boundaries are?

C: Yeah. I think, to this idea of toggling and moving things around, it really does show what is important to you in the classroom space. If pushing something to one side, it means that you have to push another to the lesser side, right, so maximizing here means that I'm not going to maximize this other thing. Then you do have to make that decision: "Am I going to spend time in the classroom letting the students discuss and ask questions, or am I going to, not lecture, but spend that time with me talking to them and they're thinking about the material outside of the classroom?" So you really can't have both. You are either talking about the material in that space at that moment in time or you say "your homework will help you understand all of these things." It's a choice. I'm not saying which one is good or bad, but it is a choice, and that's a decision that folks are making in the classroom daily. And we have to recognize that.

The more we're practicing [radical grace] explicitly and putting it to our mind, the less we have to consciously think about it. It's a habit.

So, for this idea of radical grace, once you think about what grace looks like in your classroom space, be it a seminar class, be it a large lecture, be it a small major course, then you think about those systems that you're toggling. Maybe in a seminar class, it makes sense to just talk about a topic and have the students in the classroom space work together on understanding it. Then coming back. Maybe in a research course, you're reading the material together and everyone is talking at the same time.

There is discussion and discovery. But we have to think about what grace looks like in the spaces for us, what works for our population, and be flexible.

M: I've been researching on creativity, and I believe so strongly in mathematical creativity. It's getting to the point where the reactions in the classroom are intuitive. I'm looking at the situation, and I'm going, "oh my gosh, how can I figure out a way to get four or five people to share their creativity." And that's the same thing I think about with grace. The more we're practicing it explicitly and putting it to our mind, the less we have to consciously think about it. It's a habit.

C: Yes. And I want to go back to your original question about breaking trust. I think that we sometimes reverse that on our students. This breaking of trust – "Well, what if the student breaks your trust? I can't trust them any-more." Instead of reflecting on what happened and how we can rebuild.

You can't take advantage of something that's yours.

I don't even know – I keep trying to think of a scenario where a student breaks your trust, and it doesn't happen when you have radical grace because you've had conversations with the students and you're not thinking about them breaking your trust. You're thinking about what's going on with them as an individual. We know students that think "if I mess up, that's it for me. This teacher won't try to help me anymore." I had a student who needed more time to turn in assignments and they were so worried and said "I hope you don't think I'm taking advantage of you." No, this is *yours*. You can't take advantage of something that's yours. Imagine if you have a car and you say "oh my gosh, I'm just taking advantage of driving my car all the time." No, it's yours. It's for all of you – this is not like a special thing I'm giving you. You all have this. It's for everyone.

But we have put in our students' minds that if they ask for support or help or need more stuff, they're taking advantage, and I think that's probably what she was talking about. "If I give my students these chances, will they take them?" That is usually what happens when you give someone something.

M: What does a teacher *lose*? I'm saying this because I had this mentality to be honest, like I had this scarcity mentality, this adversarial mentality. That you can only ask twice or you can only do this. And I bet you, it was in grounded right from K through 12.

C: It is, because you know when we were younger you had to ask to go to the bathroom, right? Yes. And sometimes the teacher would say "No. You've already gone enough times." So there is this scarcity of asking for something. It is put into your psyche that in the classroom you can't ask for something too many times.

M: Instead of asking like "hey, are you feeling okay? You might need to go to the nurse." Even just giving them a chance to freely move. I swear to you this happened this semester, where a student had to go to the restroom. And he said to me, "I really have to go to the bathroom. Here, I'm going to take my Apple watch and put it down. I'm going to put my phone on the table and everything," and I was just like, "Go. You have to go." They felt it was a necessity, and this is an incoming student. They felt it was a necessity to put all of their devices down so that I could trust them. We do that so often, and I mean "we" like the collective educators. You know, bringing the doctor's note, prove to me that you need these things, prove to me that something's going on with you, so I can trust you. And you know those like catching stories are water cooler talk. Those, catching stories are the ones that are being passed around. "This person said that their grandfather was passed, but I saw them at the grocery store."

C: Right. "How dare they! They're gonna go grocery shopping when their grandfather died?!"

M: First, if they made it up, then there has to be something else that is their impetus for making it. You're having difficulties somewhere.

C: Right, and they don't trust you enough to say that to you.

M: That's right. And so you can approach things so many different ways. It's weird that we have to approach it with kindness, with support, and that is *radical*. It reminds me of those online-proctored exams that you have to be in the camera, you have to do this, no one else can be in the space. How about changing the tests?

C: Now, come on! Whoa, whoa, whoa! Yeah you're just throwing it all off. How do I know what they know when I'm not steadily watching them do this thing?

M: But this hits me as more of a systemic, institutional issue. Because, to me, if you want me to change to online instruction, you gotta give me time to think about it. First of all, at my institution, there are people who took their spring break to adjust because it got transferred over to online learning during the pandemic. Many faculty took the whole spring break to situate themselves to try to figure out how to do online learning and to situate others. I mean, there was a whole canvas module on this, and people were talking to each other and getting set up. That, to me, was so tough because you've gone eight, nine weeks straight and then you're being asked to *not* have a break, but rather situate yourself, so that you could go another eight, nine weeks. That's tough! So, as I said, you can change your test questions, but that also requires you reading, thinking, or making sure that you're comfortable with changing those test questions yourself. That is an institutional thing – that is where someone goes to you and says, "hey, we're going to pay you X amount to take some time out to figure out what is going on and how you can modify for this new scenario."

C: I think that it's important to be very clear that this idea of radical grace, or even changing what you do in the classroom space, isn't a one-off or a quick fix. Especially if you've been at a place for a while and you have a reputation for not providing grace and support to your students. You're not going to, say in one semester, change the whole narrative to be "Oh, that person is so great. They were so kind. You can tell they really care about their students." It's not going to happen, but it can gradually change if you really are thoughtful about making the change. And I do not mean just a "thoughtful person", because I'm hopeful that all educators are thoughtful.

And I think the same is true when you switch up your way of thinking about questions to ask your students. It isn't going to be like a quick, "oh, I just rewrote all the questions and they look like this now." It does take time to massage it, and not everything works for every class. That's a local grace thing, right? In that classroom space, things are going to be different than maybe another class. You could be teaching the exact same course in one semester but just different populations. And you have to think about it differently. You change the assignments around, but you might have to change the strategy about how you talk about stuff in those classrooms. I think it's important to know that we do have to have time to do this, and it has to be valued by our colleagues. Because if it's not valued, then we don't see why we should spend time on it. In fact, time is really the only commodity we have that we can't ever get back. So we do have to think about "How do I spend this commodity that I'm never going to get back?"

M: Yes. It's also the only commodity that has a zero-sum game in our classrooms. There's only a finite amount of it. It goes back to what you said "what do you value in your 15 minutes?" Is it really what you value? Radical grace is a belief, and then I have to act to achieve radical grace as a *value*. My definitions of those two, belief and value, is from an example that Gail Tang brought up before. I want to give credit where credit's due. I can *believe* that climate change is real. But what are my *actions* doing to support that belief? I think that is the talk versus the walk as well. If we do have radical grace, how is it in every aspect?

C: Yeah, there's a lot of people talking that shit, and then you see what's happening in their classroom spaces, or the way that they talk about their students and you're just like, "Huh?" It doesn't match. The math ain't mathing.

So one of the things that I wanted to say to you because you were talking about, "He said he was sick and I saw him at the grocery store", I think that we also often forget about invisible issues.

If we create a space where the only sickness we recognize is the one we can see, we are alienating so many of our students, making them feel like they're not sick enough to ask for support, and they will quietly suffer.

Invisible, not visible to us, disabilities and issues. I think we have to remember that being sick doesn't only mean a cold and a fever. There are lots of ways that people can be sick. And if we create a space where the only sicknesses we recognize are the ones we can see, we are alienating so many of our students, making them feel like they're not sick enough to ask for support, and they will quietly suffer. And so we have to remember that, we are *whole people* and there are parts of us that don't feel well that we can't necessarily see. And many times we try to push through it.

That's not my business to decide how sick someone is. That is a different kind of doctor. I've had students that just say "I'm having a tough time". And my response is "you don't have to tell me anything. Let's figure out what you need." And this is fluid. We could say right now that you need this and then later if you need a little bit more, or something completely different. We'll figure it out, but you never have to explain to me what's going on with you if you don't feel comfortable sharing because *I believe you and I trust you*. And that just takes such a weight off, I think. Because to ask a student "what's going on?" and they have to bear their whole soul to you in order to decide whether or not it is enough... is just wild to me.

This is a little tangent but I remember, I went to a doctor. And the doctor said something racially insensitive, and I was very offended by that. So I posted on Facebook: "When you go to the doctor and they say something racist and you have to report them because it's such a violation of that relationship". And one of my friends asked "what did they say?" And I decided not to share what they said. Because I don't need someone to tell me it wasn't racist. And that happens all the time. How racist does it have to be? Do I have to say, "they said the N-word four times and then they spat on me!" That's racism. But the fact that the cashier put my change on the counter instead of in my hand when I went bought something so they wouldn't have to touch my hand... that's not enough racism for you. You know what I mean? I sometimes feel like we do something similar with our students to a different degree. We need you to be bleeding in front of us, and then we can say "Okay, you have an excuse to turn in this assignment late." And that just causes more trauma. Where is our empathy?

M: Why would you want to know? I guess, maybe because I'm very empathetic, but that's hard. I'm very thankful and have a privileged life, so I'm not experiencing these things as much. I'm not saying, "please, don't ever share anything." But at the same time, I'm very thankful that some students come up to me and literally share everything. There's a trust that's set up. But it's hard. I go home and all I think about are their difficulties. We talked about this before. I want to solve the problem so badly, and I have realized that I can't all the time.

And back to the demand of the doctor's note. If that process starts hurting the trust and creating more trauma, then the opposite process creates more trust. Rather, it creates some more trust. Because they know I care and it has students thinking that they might care about what I'm doing or what I'm saying. They might now think, "I'm going to produce more, I'm going to do more, I'm going to think more about this class." It's a snowball effect either way.

C: Right, because we're not doing it for that reason, like we're doing it to help – we're doing it to be humane.

M: That's true.

C: I think it does positively impact the classroom. Or it could not and that's okay. Because it does impact that student, that person, that human being, in a way that they feel supported. The times when you feel support are the times when you feel "I can do this." And it may not only be that very thing a person is supporting you on but even just on life. "I can do life." And isn't that what we want? We don't want people walking away like, "I can't do this, no one cares and supports me." All by just saying, "Yes, whatever you need. Let's figure this out. What can I do for you?"

M: This brings me to a big discussion that we had a couple of years ago in one of my RUME classes about equity versus equality. I mean, it's right then and there, because different people are different. And they need different things. For society, or math, or all these different places are treating them differently. One student brought up the fact that, "if they gave extensions to this one person, shouldn't they give extensions to every person?" On that assignment, right? "It's not fair to the other people that this person gets an extension." And one of the other people in the class was like, *"what was fair to begin with? Where was the fairness at?"* I think that's a huge part of radical grace, is knowing that there isn't equality ever. Period. Now, can we think about *where* can we be more equitable?

There's a feeling where actions seem to either need reciprocation, or feel like a situation of "if I do this, I will not be able to do this." Especially with students that are losing loved ones, it takes radical grace to shift to *their* needs at the moment, and not the math or other classroom aspects that we require of them. We are not arbiters of their grief, and we do not lose much at all from adjusting ourselves and our course for their difficulties. However, they gain trust and a sense of support from our actions which may help ease their pain. Radical grace does not need requirements to meet; it is not a zero-sum, scarcity game.

Chapter XIV

What is the Lasting Impact of Radical Grace?

W E CAN IMPLEMENT THE IDEAS OF RADICAL GRACE, and get into the day-to-day details, but many of the effects of radical grace will occur after the class is done. Our implementation can also be holistic, considering the radical grace we see in all aspects of academia, and how we can figure out what we truly value. In this chapter, we discuss the lasting impact radical grace can have on our students and ourselves.

M: How much do you help them "play the game," versus how much do you just say "eff it?"

C: I mean, I guess, you know, it's hard. I go back and forth with this a little bit. Because when I first was doing this, like just trying to teach in a style that is graceful, I was realizing that we're not pushing through as much material as everyone else is. And it's like, "Oh, am I doing them a disservice by doing this?" And then the other idea is like, "Am I doing a disservice by telling them I care about them?" Because they are gonna go to these other classes, and the instructor there may not care in the same way. And they're gonna be like, "Oh, it was so different." And then I came to a couple of conclusions. One is that it is not my job to prepare students to feel uninspired or to feel zero joy in someone else's class. Like, if I had this class and a student has been successful in my class, and they're not successful in your class, that has nothing to do with me. That is something that you need to think about and figure out. You need to reflect on why the students who did well in the previous class are not doing well in yours. I think we don't do that. We are like, "Oh, well, they just didn't prepare you." I think that idea is creating animosity between colleagues, versus you just thinking, "Okay, I should reflect and think about ways to adjust my course." Because I think a lot of time, the finger is pointed at the previous instructor. And sure, if someone took a look at what happened in the previous class and it is like "Did you say you just colored in a adult coloring book that day? But the lesson that week was supposed to be about the chain rule?!" then yes, that I think should give us all some pause. But if material is being covered and creativity is being fostered, the skills should map nicely to the next class. And if it doesn't, what is happening in that next class that you're not actually tapping into the skills of the students?

M: So you're talking about the juxtaposition between your class and the subsequent class, right? I also have a hard time with the juxtaposition between playing and being creative in class. And then giving them these two hour tests or 50-minute tests that are coordinated, right? And I'm having a really hard time: Should I just lean in to all of this and go with what the coordinator says and give it my little flair, or my little spin? Or do I like, take that 12% of freedom about what goes on in class to totally revamp their approaches. I'm not sure where I lie in all of this. Yeah… there are a lot of students who complain that all of this stuff that we did in class doesn't matter, because the test has us doing these chain rule questions. And the test has all of these like, you know, calculating derivatives. And so when I'm like, "Hey, can you give me *your* example of a derivative?" They're gonna be like, "Yeah, but it doesn't matter." Because what is being valued? The 88% is all of these hard and fast skills.

C: Yeah, it's hard, right!? And this is a thing that I've thought about a lot with assessment, because I'm so used to reading assessments that are co-written and thinking "Am I actually measuring, in the appropriate way, what I am asking students to do? Am I going to ask them to do some-

You need to reflect on why the students who did well in the previous class are not doing well in yours.

thing completely different in a more stressful environment than anything I've ever asked them before?" And this is something that I've gone back and forth with other people about is like, because we will act like, "Oh, I'm going to ask them this really creative, tough question on the test to stretch their mind." Like, why would you do it there when you could do it on the homework which is a less-stressful environment? Like, all you're gonna get for that answer is test anxiety, or even math anxiety, because we are not really building them to think quickly on their feet in a timed environment. So I do understand that idea of your teaching philosophy being one way and the coordinated space not allowing for that to be something that you do. Do you have enough, say, "clout" to adjust the assessments? This is hard with coordination. Because then, I mean, the way that you're probably coordinating is everyone's teaching their own class. But the assignments are the same. We coordinate a little differently, like we all meet, and we discuss and we figure out what's going to be happening that day in class, we create a mutual schedule. And so the students can talk across sections and all this stuff, because they're all in the same spot learning very similar things. And I would gather that that's not quite the same thing that's happening with you?

M: Especially the size of our university, getting a large amount of teachers together, and getting them to agree. I think it's a hard thing. And so everybody is defaulted to the coordinator. And I think that she's doing an incredible job. It's just tough.

I also participated in a large grant and used their materials, and I loved them. My hat goes off to everyone in that program, but it was really tough for me. Implementing something that's given to me requires me to know what's behind or underneath all of these assessments. That's, selfishly, why I create many of my notes, many of my discussions, and so forth, because I know what kind of goals I want to get to. And so that is, I think, another thing that's going to be a little bit hard for me. I can easily take materials and teach from them. I can go up and just say "Hey, you do some of these problems, we'll do one or two problems together and then that's it." I also feel like the opportunity gets lost, like you said, to even semi-prepare students for their future classes.

C: Yeah, I get it. I mean, this is a hard thing. But I think I gotta say, in this sort of scenario, defaulting to the coordination is what you have to do. Because I think you're right, I think you do put the students at a disadvantage when you don't. It also makes it more difficult for the coordinator, because you can have this one person that's like "I'm going to do whatever I want." And because the coordinator is working very hard, it can feel disrespectful. But having open discussions with them about some of your philosophies, I think helps impact how that course can change over time, for sure, and the 12% that you have can still be quite amazing, like art show, reflection journals, things like that. Adding in some of the creativity assignments to sort of push boundaries with them. That's also what I was able to do when I was a participant of the Creativity Research Group (CRG). And the students really liked it. Perhaps that's how you could start? But then also sharing with the coordinator: "Hey, I'm doing these things and the students really like it. And here's how we can assess it when it comes to exams and things." That does give it a larger push forward so that the next time you do it, it feels easier. And then the next time, and then next.

M: I'm not frequently a Calculus 1 or 2 instructor; I'm usually in the multi-variable Calculus, or I am in discrete math because my research previously was in proof. But you're right. There's also a big power dynamic that I want to make sure that I'm deferring, because the coordinator is a renewable-term faculty. I never want to make their lives frustrating at all. It's tough, though. Even tougher, because I've got an honors course and then this other coordinated course, that's the same content, but the honors course I can do what I want. And so, I don't know, it's a lot of soul searching.

C: Yeah. I wonder, though, because you have the two classes, that gives you the opportunity to show the difference in the methods that you do in both classes, right? Like, yes, even though with honors I think people assume "Oh, well, honors, these are the best students. So of course, you can do that." Even just across a couple of different assignments, like give them the same kind of creativity task or same assignment, and assess how you see the impact with both classes. To just carry a bit more weight, not that you need anymore, but people like data. And I agree, I think being careful about the power dynamic with the the faculty member that is renewable term. You do want to support them and help them keep their job. Often, what can happen is when those of us who have tenure say things, it just carries so much more weight for some reason. And then people think "Oh, well, we just won't hire that person back if you think they're not doing a good job right now." So you have to respond with "I just want to change something. I think they're doing a great job." So maybe having a conversation with the coordinator and talking about the things you want to try.

M: Yeah, we'll see. I think yeah, I think I'm definitely not a person that will frustrate or fight anybody and I think that's why. I'm an "everybody come together, please." I think that's why I got chosen this time. I got a question for you. What does radical grace look like with only 12% of the grade allotted to you?

C: That's a really great question, because radical grace is a teaching philosophy and how do you respect that philosophy in a coordinated setting? I think it shows up in the places and things that you have the most power over. And you have the most say over how you present material. You have the most power over how you interact with your students in and out of office hours. I think you even have the most say with how much grace to give when students need a little bit extra time or support. And so that's how it shows up for me when I'm in a coordinated system.

It also shows up behind the scenes when I'm talking with the other people in coordination, and giving ideas of things that we could do and sort of advocating for my students in that space. "I think that this question might be a little difficult, is there a way to rewrite it? So it's clearer, because it feels like there's lots of ways that the students can interpret this. I want to help mitigate anxiety." We have all taking a test. We know how that feels, right!? When you sit down and you read a question like, "What is this even asking?" And immediately, you start to panic because you're like, "Oh my God, how do I not know what this is asking? I must know what this is asking. I think it's asking this... I'll just try something." You just feel awkward. Maybe I am telling on myself! Hahahaha! I mean, I've even had students who are doing everything correctly, and they're just like, "I don't, I wasn't sure what you're asking. But I think it's this and I think you do this, but I could be wrong. I don't know." And I'm like, "No, you're completely right". And the issue is that they don't feel confident in their answer. So we have to think "what is the issue with how I'm asking this question?" Radical grace shows up in those ways, for sure.

I think it's important to tell the students we have a certain structure in our class for a reason.

Also, making exams shorter to give a buffer for when anxiety kicks in during tests. During COVID, we were creating exams that were take-home. And as you know our calculus class is super-structured: we have a schedule for what we should cover every day, we have worksheets, and the homework has been already determined. I shared that I was worried that this allocation amount in the structure may be really hard for a lot of our students who are home, because we have zero clue about what their space is going to be like. And we have nothing in here that tells them, "hey, we get it that this isn't going to be a normal semester, we have this structure for a reason. But if we need to deviate from it, for you to support you, please let us know. And we will, we are happy to do it... well maybe not happy to do it, but open to doing it." And so we had to draft a statement to put on all of our syllabi. Someone had to say that to make use all aware of the importance of saying something.

I think it's important to tell the students we have a certain structure in our class for a reason. Some people really need structure, they feel comfortable with structure. There are some of us that don't, there are some of us that need something a little different. The syllabus is adapt-able, and just reach out for support from any of us, any of the people who are coordinating, and we can figure out what works best for you. And I think that's where the radical grace will show up.

Also radical grace to yourself and your colleagues – you can't go in there rogue and just be like, "I'm going to do whatever I want." It just messes things up, and it doesn't make anyone feel good when that happens. Except maybe you because you've like stood on top of the mountain and shouted out your orders. You know, like, "I've got the tablets that have what God said on them." You know what I mean? So you don't want to be that person. You want to be an advocate and support your students and colleagues. So I think that's how it shows up. That's at least how it shows up for me.

M: It reminds me a lot like parenting sometimes. Because there's a lot of power. You could go a lot of different ways with how you react as a parent to what a kid does. Sometimes, I know I didn't react the best way. But I've been learning a lot more from that. One of the things I've learned is that I've turned up the dial infrequently with my power and been commanding, but I know that when I say, "look, this is enough", when I do turn it up a little bit, people really concentrate because they rarely have ever seen me do it.

C: I think to that, I mean, we always have to think about lasting impact. I mean, it's hard. The self-reflection in the moment is hard. It's weird, because I should know this, because it's one of those things that happens as a single person at any department. The fact that I currently don't have children... to my knowledge. That is what I've always wanted to say: "I don't have any children that I know of". And people will read this and say "that's not how that works." Anyway, people just assume I don't have anything else going on and that I can do all of this extra service. Like, "oh, well, this thing happens after four and all the parents are home because they pick their kids up. So since you're not going to be doing anything, can you take care of it? You go to the meeting instead." And I think: "What?! That is prime Netflix time. Are you kidding me?"

M: You joke, but that's needed to live, to survive, right? It's not just the moments of full work, but it's also the moments of incubation sometimes.

C: Yeah. That is what one of my colleagues tweeted once. It was so funny. I think it was like, "forget proving a theorem when you're drunk..." (I guess there are some "famous" mathematicians that do that shit...) Anyhow, he concluded: "how about proving a theorem when you're taking care of a five-year-old all day," something like that? And I thought: "Let them know!" And then I saw him the other day, and I was just like, "I love that tweet." And he was like, "you know, the thing that's wild is I'll be just playing with my son all day, watching him, and in my mind, I'm thinking of the mathematics. I put him to bed and then I work on it in the evening and it's like, there is that moment where your subconscious is unraveling these things because you've had a moment to like rest and not just keep punching, punching, punching up this hole." There are some times where you have to let stuff soak. Marinate, right? We don't think about that rest as productivity. I started telling people that rest has to be a part of work. Play is the opposite of work, and rest is not the opposite of work. Rest is a part of work – we have to incorporate that.

Do I do that? Have I taken my own medicine? Now, there are some times when I'm tired but I have to get so much done. And then I hear my little voice in the back: "you can rest. You can rest today and get nothing accomplished except for the rest and that's fine."

Play is the opposite of work, and rest is not the opposite of work. Rest is a part of work – we have to incorporate that.

M: So here's where it's going to be a full-on privilege display. But to be honest, in grad school, there would be times where I would do woodworking. Because I wanted to take a break and do some low- to medium-level work. It's also like, I have to be concentrated on the woodworking because I don't want to lose my hands. And therefore it really gives a disconnect to what I'm trying to do. And that's tough. That's tough, because a lot of times there are some scenarios where I have this action in the classroom. And then I have to just sit and reflect on it for two days. Because I was like replaying it in my head and analyzing my actions. Did I do this right? What should I have done there? Could I have done this different?

I've got another question: A lot of your thoughts on radical grace, I could take and apply them to history, or to chemistry, to English. Where do you think mathematics fits in? Is there a radical grace that's specific to math? Is there a subset?

C: Well, I think maybe "no," only because the idea of radical grace is a teaching philosophy. So like, if you're a teacher, this is a philosophy that you can use. I think the thing that may make it a bit unique for mathematics is that we really have to think differently about our assessments and the ability to give students opportunities to rewrite. And this often already is built in with a lot of humanities classes. Like, "okay, here's your first draft." And we don't do that. We don't necessarily do that in mathematics. We're just like, "one shot. Good luck." And so changing maybe that idea of assessments within the pedagogy with this philosophy of "I'm going to give you more opportunities."

I think with mathematics, adding some of the things that come from the humanities is good, reflections, summarizing things. I think, Miloš, you do really great projects with your students about how to summarize the things they've learned in creative ways. That doesn't often happen, I think. And so the thing is, it's always so funny to me when people would be like, "I don't let them have cheat sheets," which please don't call them cheat sheets. They are resource pages, because if you're letting them have it, it's not a cheat sheet. Can we change the narrative there? But we don't even really do that enough. Allow students to write out a summary of the things that they've learned so far to really get a good picture of maybe even how things are all connected. I think that's one of the big issues we have in mathematics – people don't see how connected mathematics is to so many different things. You see these memes or jokes on Twitter, and it's like, "I wish I had learned how to do taxes instead of the quadratic formula." Because there's no understanding of why you actually learn the quadratic formula, what good it does, things like that. We say "just memorize this thing" without any motivation. I think with including radical grace, we often sit back and think "why am I doing what I'm doing in the way that I'm doing it? Who is it supporting? Who is it harming? What's happening long-term?" All of those reflection questions have to come up when you're including radical grace. And I think when you do that the mathematics curriculum will change.

For me, in my journey, the more I've learned, the harder teaching is for me.

M: It is like writing a mathematical proof. You want the end goal? And you have some assumptions. And you kind of want to write the reasons. What will happen at the end if you do this or have counter arguments? You are thinking about the whole scenario but it takes time. It takes time literally sitting down, sometimes. For me, in my journey, the more I've learned, the harder teaching is for me. It's even more of a time of reflecting because my eyes are open a little bit more.

C: It becomes difficult in a different way.

M: I think it's funny. Going back a little bit, we talked about assessments in our classrooms. But I think there needs to be a change in assessments for us as faculty. Because to me, if I need to sit and think about and reflect on teaching, it's got to be part of my, how I'm being assessed. Sometimes, unfortunately, all of these faculty evaluations and so forth, that are done in the department are a little bit of a checkbox-type thing. And I wonder, what would happen if, you know, you asked questions about, "when did you give grace?" Could you imagine? When did you care? When did you show support for your students? When did you show support for your colleagues?

C: When did you show support for yourself? Let's really do this.

M: This, to me is more important than how many tests I had in the class or what textbook I used.

C: Yeah, that shit doesn't matter. I agree. The hard part, though, is I'm having this conversation now about the, what is it called, like DEI (Diversity, Equity, and Inclusion) statements that people have to write now to get hired. We don't know how to really assess questions like this, and we don't support people. We don't teach people how to do this work or write up what they're doing. You just get fake stuff. And you just get people reading it later and thinking "yeah, that sounds good." You know what I mean? We have to include in this process, the training, and we don't. We just always assume everyone knows how to do everything. Just think about how much training people get to teach period.

M: As we're going down the advising path. It's not just the advising path, I think, to me, it's a question of our field. And how our field positions and reacts to a lot of these things. How do you evaluate a teaching statement? How do you evaluate research statements?

C: Right. I think the way I have been taught to evaluate research statements is: How clear is it? What did we understand from it? Do we see this research as ongoing? Is there evidence that this will be productive person as a researcher at our institution? That's what we sort of look for.

With teaching we look for the things that mimic what we're already doing. "Oh, this person really thinks about the students. You can tell they care." We look for stuff like that. Like, "oh, wow, they really think about teaching. They reflect on it a lot in their statement," which people can just write. But how do you do that with a DEI statement? Because everyone is doing research, everyone is thinking about teaching, but not everyone is thinking about DEI work. And many people don't have the privilege not to think about it. What do you do with that person? And the person who has not thought about DEI at all... what do you do with them? And of course, this could never happen with any of these other statements. People will say "Wow, we shouldn't get rid of the best candidate. Because they haven't done any DEI stuff. Some people don't have the opportunity to do it." And if that's the case, then why are we fucking looking at DEI statements? Because the assumption that people have thought about DEI must be a part of this, if we are asking you to write about it. So if you're gonna look me in the eyes and say, "well, this isn't quite fair, because this person hasn't been thinking about this", then please someone tell me why the fuck are we asking everyone to do it? It's performative.

So if this is something that we're going to assess, and we think is important, we need to make sure that everyone is doing it. And doing it well.

M: What do we value? That is the main question. Tell me what we value and then okay, we're gonna assess based on that. How do we value what we do then? And to me, when I'm in those conversations, I can tell specifically what we value. And it definitely is not aligned with our assessments. So yeah, I get frustrated a lot because I want everybody to be on the same page with a lot of this, but it doesn't happen. What do we as a group value, maybe it has to be a majority thing, because I also get really frustrated with the metrics to be honest with you. If this person has X amount of papers, and this other person doesn't, but their teaching statement is incredible. They're DEI statement, which we do not have at our school yet. We wanted to make sure that we had a DEI statement before making sure that we request others. Anyways, what are the metrics here? To me, this spills into a lot of other evaluative scenarios. So graduate students – what do we value in graduate students? A lot of that just frustrates me because I have been in scenarios that if I were the graduate student applying, I would not get it. And here I am in the scenario seeing myself not being able to get in.

C: I think this happens a lot in academia. Especially on the recognition side when prizes are involved.

M: I had a student come to my office at the end of a semester, not the semester that I taught them. But this semester afterwards, came to my office, and delivered the letter that they use to nominate me for a teaching award. And they said, "you did not get it. But I wanted you to know how much you impacted not only me, but all of us that were on this letter."

It reminded me of a colleague that after looking at my curriculum vita (CV) said to me, "Why do you put the grants that weren't funded on your CV?" And I said, "Look, I know that I did a lot of work for those grants. So whether they were funded or not funded, I want to know that I did that work on that time." And that CV is a reflection of 40 hours a week. You know, 50 weeks out of the year. That's what that CV is a reflection of everything. Good, bad, in between, even the papers that are stuck in limbo are down at the bottom on unfinished papers, right? I don't want to be the person who, and I was this for first few years, doing a lot of stuff. Then I came into the evaluative process and went, "Oh, I had two papers this year or one paper or no papers this year. And it feels like I failed." When honestly, I took four months to really write and polish a grant proposal.

Anyway, the nomination thing is such a big deal. It hit me so hard. This student took his time, and he wrote a letter. An actual paper letter. That, to me, is bigger than trophies. Bigger than academic awards. Getting an email from a student, that is now a teacher, that says "Hey, can we talk?" or "hey, can you share some of your resources?" The student that when I call up the pizza shop, they're like, "oh, it's Dr. Savić. I had the best time at your class. And I learned a lot." My gosh, it's energy. It hits me. I want to take that and share with the new generation. That's my big deal. Now I'm thinking of ways of channeling every aspect to the new generation. What can I do to give opportunities for students?

At the graduate level? At the postgraduate level? I've got a friend of mine, who is still tenure-track, non tenured yet. What can I do if opportunities come to me that I could defer to them? I feel like I'm the past. And there's a huge future out there. I could do one of two things: hoard all of that future, or I can be the one putting ladders everywhere else for people to climb up. I'm here, I'm at this situation. How can others come here? How can I help them get a ladder so that they can get to wherever they want to go?

I think part of it is humanistic to me. And if we don't, I mean, this sounds like a warning. But if we don't become more humanistic, we're done. We're done as a field, we're done as a teaching profession. We're done everywhere. Because if people still perceive math as being non-humanistic,

If we don't become more humanistic, we're done. We're done as a field, we're done as a teaching profession.

then AI (artificial intelligence) is going to teach people how to do the quadratic formula, then AI is going to teach people how to do algebraic topology.

C: Or AI is just gonna do those things. Do you know what I mean? Like we can create AI to put in something and it does the math for us. Yeah. There's gonna be no need really to have mathematicians doing any of this work. Because you can just have computers do it. We don't have human calculators anymore. So what what are we thinking here?

M: What is our use? Who are we? And to be honest, that kind of humanity and grace, that is who we are. And that can be reciprocated generation after generation after generation. Much more than anything else, much more than content.

Do we think about what our teaching does for students 20 years from now? Generations from now? Thinking about radical grace involves thinking about what will last from the 16 weeks, or year, or multiple years your students will be in your course. Teaching with radical grace requires consideration that students may not have been shown grace previously, and to be transparent about class structure. Finally, we have to think about the lasting impact of radical grace on ourselves, and to incorporate activities that allow for us to rest and play.

CHAPTER XV

WHAT DOES RADICAL GRACE LOOK LIKE IN THE FUTURE?

WE IMAGINE A FUTURE WITH GRACE, without it being radical, because grace is hopefully baked into academia. But that requires reflection of ourselves, being flexible with future classrooms, and practicing radical grace in many situations. One aspect is certain: we cannot fully practice radical grace without practicing it for ourselves. This is our wide-ranging discussion on the future (and present) of radical grace in our classrooms.

C: So what do you think it looks like when grace is no longer radical? When we don't need to say the term "radical grace?"

M: Right. So, first things first, we will be flying in those Jetson cars during that time. Honestly, I really don't know. I think I don't know, off the top of my head, because to me, it's really hard to see it. All I hear is about all the difficulties that students are going through. But maybe if it were ubiquitous, maybe if it were in academia, I could see it being more of education being conversations that stimulate growth. It's not about hitting all these check marks, hitting all these content spaces, but rather, trying to develop a person for the future. I saw this stat that said that like a third of college graduates are going to get a job that they had no idea or no preparation for. So, okay, that's understandable, because the way technology is working, the way we're working, and we're changing and having different modes, right, there needs to be some kind of flexibility. I also saw another thing that said that people are switching careers at around three or four times the amount that people did through 30 years ago. You would have a career, that you would just be there, you'd be in that same place for 40 years, hit the retirement button, and then, "see you later." Yeah, right. And now it's not only different careers, you're moving to different places or you're also having dual careers or doing some kind of part-time freelance. It's becoming more individualized. But to me, all of that is surrounded with a belief in oneself that they can do it. And that starts with fostering that in the classroom. I can't believe in myself, unless I feel like someone else is believing in me.

C: Yeah, I mean, it definitely would change the dynamic of how we interact in the classroom with our students, and what education looks like for sure. And I think you're completely right. I think in a situation with radical grace, you are preparing students for any kind of career, or preparing them to be in spaces or careers where they know they can succeed, because they've spoken

In a situation with radical grace, you are preparing students for any kind of career... where they know they can succeed, because they've spoken up so much.

up so much. They've been supported in these ways that they did get to branch out, they did get to try new things, they did get to learn new skills. They got the opportunity to stretch their muscles, if you will. And now they can think "okay, this is a new thing. This is a new thing and it is hard. But I've done hard things before. I have done new things before. I can do this." This is without feeling a lasting panic that stops them from moving forward. I think to this point, what we're doing, when we talk about radical grace in the classroom, is moving away from this, "everybody has to get the exact same thing" situation to a more equitable way of teaching. Maybe a bit more individualized. "Sure I'm in the space with more folks, but I, as an individual, still see myself in the space, and my unique needs can still be met." I think about this as similar to the first way we used to do education, right? The master and the apprentice. There's a one-on-one relationship. And I completely get why that is not a good situation. It is exclusionary and would make it so only a few folks get the opportunity to learn. And what we're doing now is we have the opportunity for everyone who can to get knowledge, that is often shared only in one way. But there's got to be a middle ground where you still have the positives, the pros of the one-on-one approach, and the inclusion and opportunity for everyone to learn. To address individuality while being in a classroom of 40 or 200. And I think that's what it would look like, if radical grace was no longer radical.

M: Yes, if grace was just there. We brought this up in a separate conversation, but the fulcrum, the balance, and highlighting individuality are really important. But I also think radical grace in a classroom highlights collective individuality. This notion where you can bring yourself to a community. Yes, you're improving your own individuality, but you can also bring yourself because the space, the feeling, that you have in there is one of grace. That we're not equal, we're not on the same plane when it comes to a lot of separate things, but what we can do is figure out what's going on with each other and try to lift each other up. And that's a big deal to me. Like, that's exactly it.

There's even power dynamics, when you go into a group. You're in a group of four - the time you turn around your desk, that first time, everybody's trying to figure out what's going on with that group, where they're at, what they can say, and what they can't say, what's going on here, and everything else. But in a classroom with radical grace, week seven, okay, a little bit of the guard is down. Because people feel more comfortable. We talked about that before. If we have a whole institution that thinks about teaching with radical grace, the default is to come in and be yourself. You're more apt to try stuff, you're more apt to screw up, you're more apt to figure things out. And can you imagine a whole institution that, like, it's not a major of mathematics, it's mathematics and grace. It's not the major of history, its history with grace. Where you're not only learning these content level skills, you're also learning interpersonal and intrapersonal skills.

C: It creates a community. So it's like, it's not just an institution. Whatever that means, and that word "institution" can carry so much weight. But it also can create a community of learners that are creating a space where there's grace, creating a space where you have support, creating a space where you can bring your whole self to that community because there is a spot for you. And there's often not that space in these institutions of higher learning, these academic settings such that you're thinking "I don't see myself there. I don't feel welcome." And it's not how people are speaking, necessarily. No one has said to you, "You don't belong here." But the actions of the community are spaces that say, "You can't do this. You can't be there." Because the vibe I'm getting from that space is saying that. And with having grace not be radical, it is saying there is a space, a spot, for everyone here. Every body belongs here. This is a community. And it is true about academia - everyone belongs there. Everyone should have a space there. And we have done this thing where we kept the elitism of the master-apprentice thing, but made it on a grander scale.

M: We talked about leadership, and thinking about what it means to be a leader. You can give speeches or you can talk, but actions are gigantic. Especially when things hit the fan. What actions are happening when you fall down, even as a leader? What actions are happening? I just think about spaces that I've walked into where, you know, I didn't say a word, nobody said a word. But then five minutes in somebody is like, "oh, here we go again." in a demeaning way. And that's five minutes in. That person was comfortable with this kind of negativity in this public space right away. And so, I think a lot about that. I'm a huge believer in the environments that we co-create. I think a lot about walking through a door and the "feel" I get when I do that. When I walk into my house, how do I feel? When my students walk into my classroom, how do they feel? Is it anticipatory excitement? Is it dread, right? Even when they click the link, the Zoom link, what do they feel about it? It happens gradually at first. We don't know what the expectations are on both ends. Three weeks, four weeks in, we get a little bit of understanding, maybe six weeks, and so forth. How do I feel when I'm on a campus? Is there radical grace? Is there grace around this campus? Or do I feel very "pulled back?" All of this comes into play. And I don't know if I've ever told you this, but I feel like teaching is 90% psychological and 10% content? If I saw a future with radical grace, could you imagine how much of the psychology would be not as big of a percentage? Because once you've set up some kind of psychological grace environment in the class, then you can throw in other content with less difficulty. And it's totally fine with people. It's like, "hey, look, we're not expecting this, we're not expecting that! Let's just play around with this and see what happens."

C: It allows for the creativity to come out, because you no longer have that psychological barrier. I mean, there are a lot of people that are coming to our classes that have been traumatized by past classes. So we have to work that much harder to get over that big wall of trauma for them to feel safe. I think in the future with grace not being radical and grace just being the starting point, the baseline, the default in your class means you're thinking about "how do I not cause trauma that this student will carry to every single class they have later?" So that when they are in that next class, the work that has to be done to break down the trauma is lessened. So they do feel that freedom to learn more. One of the ways I think we have to do that, and I think you hit on this, is this idea of power. That idea of when someone's coming into a space, how do they feel? And we have so much power to make that space, a space where someone feels uncomfortable, feels scared, feels worried, feels stressed and drags themselves in, and not excited to be there. We have that power. And we have the power to create the complete opposite. And so there are ways that we can create that, that space that everyone wants to be in, when we release some of that power, and say, "let's create this space together." And that, I think, is what a radical grace classroom looks like in the future. One where you've created, as a group, this amazing space that folks feel ready to join, feel that they, they see themselves in that space, that space is for them, because they helped create it.

M: Their thinking is valued. They're being listened to. They can co-create with others, they can try stuff. I think over over the course of the last few years, especially when it comes to COVID and everything else, speaking with people, and you know, talking with us, radical grace has permeated into different aspects

The default in your class means you're thinking about "how do I not cause trauma that this student will carry to every single class they have later?"

of my life. It's weird, we're talking about teaching, but there's now radical grace that I'm providing in the grocery store, with interacting with others, even with my family. It's just this little notion of, I don't know, maybe it does come back from competitiveness, or negativity or etc, etc. But once I've said, "Okay, I've had enough of all this. Oh, I'm sure that this person is having a hard time today. Maybe they cut me off because they're having a difficult time." And I would be like, so frustrated at 17, 18, 19. And I kind of saw it as well, there was a modeling of that frustration. But afterwards, it's just this small amount of frustration in my life. It's not going to be there forever; it's going to dissipate. So why not give a bit of grace to others? To me, that might be a byproduct of the future of having radical grace be institutionalized. Yeah. Then now you're going with "Oh, okay. Where can we go from here? Maybe this is the bubble, the academic bubble. But it doesn't have to be."

C: I like that idea. Because I think you're spot on, right? This idea of how we treat and see our students. It doesn't make sense to not also think about just people this way, right? There's nothing that changes. Once we leave that classroom, we're like, "okay, we're out of the classroom, I don't have to care about any of the other people. I just had to care about these 25 to 200 students." When it's not something you turn on and off. It's something you have. And you think about, because you're not just providing grace to your students, you are providing grace to yourself. And when you start providing grace to yourself, you're doing that in all these moments, which means you're also providing grace to other people in the space as inherent.

M: Follow up question, and let's do it right now. It may be a chicken and egg question.

C: We know the answer to that though. The answer to that is the egg came first. Because the predecessor of the chicken laid an egg that hatched into a chicken. So that's it. My students taught me that. They were like, "we know the philosophical Friday answer. Oh, okay." I was like, "what?" And then she said that answer, and I was like, "how could you be so smart?" Because it makes sense.

M: It really does. Do we need to provide ourselves radical grace before we provide to others?

C: Why not at the same time?

The kind of radical grace we have to give ourselves is forgiveness.

I think though, we've talked about this a little bit: what does radical grace look like? And it does look different, depending on what you're doing in the moment. And I think the kind of radical grace we have to give ourselves is *forgiveness*. I think maybe you're right, we need to do that at the beginning. Because I think a lot of people, when they care about their students, they beat themselves up over "small" things. I mean, everything has an impact. We don't know the ripple effect of things that we say or do. But I think about those things and carry those things. And it's really hard to forgive ourselves. I think we're, people say this, "you're your worst critic." And I think that that's the grace we have to give ourselves to recognize, "no, you are also a whole person." And that's really the foundation, you're a whole person. So the grace you give yourself is your whole person. Everyone makes mistakes. What did you learn from that? We can do this. Let's move on. And so maybe you have to do that first to start the work. But it's also a thing you have to continue to do. Because it's not like, "I feel so much better." Like, "stop being so hard on yourself." "Oh, that's it? Oh, that's all I had to do?" You know, it's a continuous thing.

M: Instead of a checkbox. I think about that quite frequently. You know, we have the chapter on "stories that shaped us." And there are so many difficult stories in there. And ones that like, I can't take back. And so I have to realize that I can't take them back. But I can change what can go on forward.

C: You can learn from them. Yeah.

M: They're almost semi-haunting in a way, because they always come back up. But there's also new stories that I've made. And honestly, this may be something that could be a part of change in academia is the celebration of things that are going well with the same amount as the frustration with the things that aren't going well. And I am the first person that will get down on myself for everything. But when something good happens, I'll be like, "Oh, okay," and then move on to the next one.

C: I think because we have made excellence the default. So if you fall below excellence, how dare you? You didn't even reach the default. We have decided that. And so when we are excellent, we're like, "Well, of course, this is what I'm supposed to be doing. What other thing am I supposed to be doing?" And we've had these kinds of conversations about our lives, or our personal lives. Someone's like, "Oh, you're doing this great thing," and personally, you're like, "I don't understand another way. How else are you supposed to do it?" And so we've done the same thing with teaching with these sorts of things in academia. We don't realize the impact that we're having. And so when we're having this really positive impact, "of course that's supposed to happen. I can't get patted on the back for doing the thing I'm supposed to do." But when we don't do the thing we think we're supposed to do, we believe we should be punished and we do it to ourselves.

> *I think because [academia has] made excellence the default. So if you fall below excellence, how dare you?*

M: We're going into it now. This is all – it bundles with forgiveness, but it's all radical grace on oneself. And I think a lot about that, only recently, have I allowed myself to say thank you after a compliment. It's only been maybe a year, year and a half. It's usually "Oh yeah, that's not me," or, "oh, no, no, that can't be right." It's not even humbleness. It's kind of outright incredulous-ness. And only recently have I accepted it. Even in emails, I'm now saying, "well, thank you for those kind words." But why? They're giving courteous goodwill to me. And I'm here rejecting the same things that I want to give or provide in my classroom. What am I doing?

We deserve compliments as whole people. We deserve feedback. We deserve the time for reflection. We deserve to be celebrated. We deserve all of that.

C: We have to know we deserve it, and that's the hardest part. We have to know we deserve it. And I think it's a mirror because our students do the same thing. Like, my students will say, "I'm sorry, I keep asking for more things. I'm going through a lot." And I said, "this is yours. You do not have to be sorry, for taking what is yours. It's your right. That compliment is yours. It's just for you." This person isn't saying that to every person on the street, they're saying it to you, it's your compliment, and we deserve it. Even when we think we don't, that person thinks we do. Or else they wouldn't have said it; I wouldn't have said it. And I think that it has to be the change, that has to be the courteous goodwill we give ourselves is to know that we deserve compliments as whole people. We deserve feedback. We deserve the time for reflection. We deserve to be celebrated. We deserve all of that. And it's really hard, because we've been taught to be humble, that you're not doing anything out of the ordinary. Because the baseline, the default is excellence.

M: But then it's like, "yeah, but I didn't get this award. Or I didn't get this fellowship, or I didn't get this." And are those are the metrics that I'm going to support myself by?

C: Things I didn't get. The things I did. Not the places I succeeded, right, but the arenas I failed in, that's how I'm measuring my worth.

M: All the feels are hitting me. Maybe it is that there was so little grace in my classrooms. I was just about to say, there might have been grace in my classes, and maybe it was implicit, but it was never explicit. It was never out there. That fosters a lot of non-grace, or anti-grace, if you will, even more within. And suddenly, I'm rejecting all of these celebratory things.

I've had to concentrate really hard and unlearn to change my whole mindset. And really enjoy a lot of the situations that either I've been successful, or, and this is part of the zero-sum games, alter competitiveness, when others are having

Comparison is a killer of joy.

success around me. It's *not* this giving radical grace to myself, or anti-grace was like, "Oh, my gosh, I got the award, or I didn't get the award." And they did. And it's like, "Oh, what am I doing? Who am I?" I've had to unlearn a ton of that, to just sit down and celebrate the accomplishments that others around me have had.

C: Comparison is a killer of joy. It is a killer of joy. And we have created this space of competitive mess where we think we have to compare and be better than the person next to us instead of having this idea of grace, in the community, in the space. Then, we would see that person's success as a success to the whole. And we'll be so proud of that person's success because it's *our* success. Meaning as a group, we have created a space for that where that person can be successful. That they can be their full selves. And that is huge, because those spaces exist.

M: Are you ready? Now do that in the classroom. This exact same thing we talked about in our field, in academia, take that and put that in the class.

C: There's this amazing thing that my students will do in office hours. They'll ask me WeBWorK questions. And I'll walk them through and they're showing their screen. They're doing their problem. And I'll say, "go ahead and put your answer in. So we can celebrate with you." And they do! Green pops up, and everyone claps in the office hour, or they put like a celebration of a little cheer. And we were like, congratulations. Great job on that problem.

M: I saw this on Twitter, the reactions in a classroom, Zoom reactions, are like fuel.

I have this task in my class, where it's called the productive failure. A student has done a problem in class. And they had somewhere where they got stuck, and then they did stuff to overcome it. It's worth, by the way, 5% of their grade. I'll also give alternatives so that nobody is pressured to go up and present all of this. But what they have to do is in class, every time we start class, "does anybody have a productive failure?" One person goes up to the document camera and says, "Okay, here's what I did. Here's where I messed up. And here's where I overcame it." They explain it and everything else. There was one presentation, and I wrote a paper about it, because it was so fantastic, where the student comes up, presents this proof, and, and jokes about how she wants to disprove me, that the theorem is false. She wants to disprove me and she's making it a big deal. Students are laughing. They're enjoying it. And at the end, when she figures out the proof, and she has a big OH! and is done. Everybody starts clapping like a roar. And to me, that's one of the signs that everybody's for everybody. And I don't know where we've gotten this individual... I probably do know where we've got this individualistic, "I only need to do it for myself." But when it's so synergistic, when people are giving each other grace, when people are valuing it, it feels amazing.

C: Because we know what it feels like when you *don't* have it. I mean, even in our own classes that we're teaching, it's not always been what my classes are like. My class next year won't be like that, or the next. It'll be different. Because every day, I'm sort of learning every semester, learning, "what are the things that I can keep doing? Or I should adjust a little bit? Or what more should I say?"

So we know what it feels like when the classroom doesn't have grace. And I think at the beginning, we didn't know this great feeling. And now we're feeling it, it's like, "I don't want to go back. I don't want to go back to that." And those classes were fine. But this class, like heart racing, excitement about what your students are saying, and how they're talking to each other, and things are doing so well. And you're like, we may not finish talking about this topic, but look at all the other topics we got to talk about. And so when we do come back to this, you have all these great positive thoughts that branch out.

M: Isn't that what what the model academia is supposed to be? Throwing out ideas? Philosophizing, right?

C: Teaching how to think.

M: Teaching how to think. I would add, teaching ourselves to think about how we think on our own without the instructor. Because I think teaching how to think is kind of still is difficult.

C: So I, when I say, "teaching how to think," this is what I'm thinking. Yeah. Not like, "think like me."

M: Yes, exactly. But that's the mentality, though, isn't it? And this is not just in mathematics. It's in academia, where you go to this class, and you're like, "Well, this is how I'm going to think. This is how I'm going to do architecture." And you have to balance that fostering their own ideas towards certain architecture, and providing our own perspective. I think this is a big thing: we all have some expertise. And they can lean on that at times. But there's got to be a balance between us providing all the expertise, and then learning some things on their own. If not, we're going to be creating 30 carbon-copies that think Dr. Savić's way and only do things that way. We've got one – that's plenty enough.

C: Agree.

M: HA! But seriously, though, that's the thing I think about.

What does radical grace look like for yourself now and in the future? Like, what's one thing that you can point out that you're like, even in academia, where you're like, "you know what, I gave myself some grace."

C: Forgiveness is still a bigger issue. We're still in the process. If you didn't know that all I'm doing, I'm still comparing myself to the idea of what I should be doing. "Oh, I should have done this. Oh, I should have done that. Oh, I didn't do this. I didn't do that." Without remembering that I'm a whole person. Right. And as this whole person, there's a lot of stuff I am dealing with every single day. And it was just like that day, I had to only focus on this thing. I had to focus on my mental health. And that didn't include reading email, it didn't include, writing a journal article. It didn't include these other things and included staying in bed a little longer. It included a long shower, included making dinner and eating it with my mom. And maybe those things, I didn't include the stuff I have to do for my job, but it did include the stuff I have to do *for me to do* my job.

M: It's so short-sighted, when all we can say is that I need to do this, this, this, and this for my job. Because I could do it. But I may not give my 100% because 80% of my mind is on other stuff right now. It's having a hard time. I think that the thing that I've had to learn so much is the opposite: "why is 80% of my mind occupied by that email when I'm at home?" That's what I feel like radical grace has taught me a little bit. I still have those moments, I still get extremely anxious at home, that I did not do X, Y, or Z for class, I take weekends off. I think that's the first big "radical grace" thing that I've done for myself. And that is radical in academia, wildly enough. And I still have weekends, where I'm like, "Oh, my gosh, this thing is due. I need to do it." I feel like I've done a much better job of balancing the work and home. But it is extremely conscious of me to balance it. If it were unconscious, or subconscious,

I would probably go and work on this next project for this next thing or do this other thing. It's hard.

It's so short-sighted, when all we can say is that I need to do this, this, this, and this for my job. Because I could do it. But I may not give my 100% because 80% of my mind is on other stuff right now.

C: I think a couple of things. So one, this idea that you couldn't give 100% of the thing. You could only give this much. We have to remember that's true for students also. And I think a lot of times we take it as disrespect when students don't finish an assignment we've given them in the time they are supposed to. And they're like, "I had a lot of other stuff going on." And it feels disrespectful because they didn't prioritize this assignment we gave them without thinking about. They understand the importance of these assignments. They understand what this grade means. And yet still, they chose something else. For some reason that was that way more for them. Yeah, I remember. And I don't need to know why. I just need to accept that I make those decisions also.

M: We're all adults. This might be hard to take. But the hypocrisy of getting mad at a student for not turning in their stuff. And grading it two weeks later.

C: I say, I'm so grateful for my students. They don't have to show me grace. And they do every time when I come in there. I'm like, "sorry. I don't got it for you."

M: Why? Well, why is it default? That it's okay that I don't have it for you. But that when you don't have it for me... I think that's the thing. So when when we say radical grace for myself, I think a part of that has to do with "Am I being hypocritical in these situations?" Reflection is part of the radical grace for myself.

C: The other thing when you talked about balance, I appreciate you saying that, because I think a lot of times there is this issue in academia when it comes to the balance with family that women are expected to make versus men. Right. And knowing your family dynamic, I definitely appreciate that it is not 50/50 between you and your partner, but both of you are 100/100 with your kids. And you recognize that and you're spending that time. Not on work, but with your family, because you know, it's 100/100.

M: It has to be, also know that there's a lot of things in life that are not zero-sum. But time is zero-sum. And, to me, I've gotta try the best I can to make sure that I'm enjoying that time with them when they're them. Because I know, I can just blink. And they're 18. But the same thing can be said about any other interaction I have in academia. I blink and people are gone, or people just don't want to be around. So what am I doing now? To enjoy, to foster, to support them being around here? Am I providing it to them? Am I providing it to myself to provide to them?

C: Yeah, like I think we definitely take for granted a lot of things. Well, there's tomorrow. Well, the next class, without thinking about the long term. Because it is just a blink in the grand scheme of things. We really don't think about. I think maybe it's unfair, I sometimes don't think about the impact until someone brings it up later. Someone's like, "that person does not like you. Yeah, because you said this one thing once."

M: I've had that. Not because I said something once, but because I've taught active learning. And they did not like it. This student wrote an essay, basically scathing, in the student evaluation. Lengthy, though, that was like, "this is not teaching" and all this other stuff. And I talked to friends of his that took my other classes and everything else. And you know, what I said to them? "I really appreciate his thoughts." Why? Because it's passionate. I'm okay with people who cannot stand me. And I'm okay with people who are totally fine with the class and everything. It's the middle ground that I have a hard time with, because I don't know where I stand. Think about that: even saying that I'm okay with people who hate my teaching style. I'm giving radical grace right then and there. Because I could go the total opposite way, and be frustrated with it, or be mad at them, or anything else. But I said to friends of his I go, "Look, I'm totally fine with their opinion, and they're entitled to it."

C: How do you know it was him?

M: Because we had conversations during the semester, where he had definitely told me that he cannot stand what is going on.

C: That's the other part too. The grace you showed in your classroom in that space with that student is that they felt comfortable saying to you in that time and still felt comfortable sharing that on the evaluation. Do you know what I mean? Like they personally didn't like the way the class was taught. And that's what they said. Because they knew they could say that.

M: Grace equals comfort. And those show up in those ways, right?

C: That's the thing. We can't expect every single student to just be like, "this was perfect for me. This is a great class. I loved this." But what we do want when we have radical grace is for students to be able to say how they felt. The comfort in that space? Like, "I wish we had done this, I wish we had done that."

Now, here is the thing. We all know there will be students that always feel like they can say whatever they want. And sometimes we perceive some of our students to be this way based on their identity. But what we want is for everyone to feel this comfort. And sometimes the grace that is shown is shared by everyone in the space, even those that we may think don't need it or won't provide it.

M: It kind of equates with what we talked about before with. I did this. So why are you not reciprocating it back? Like? Is it the default expectation that everyone's going to enjoy, or take, or co-create the radical grace that's going on? Is that the expectation? It's going to be hard, right?

C: We can't even get other educators to cooperate with us sometimes. And they've been teaching for a long time. They know the benefits. Especially when we talk about this, they get it, but it's still really hard. I got to care, right? I've got to spend time, I don't have time, what I'm doing is fine. People are fine. I've got no complaints.

So of course, we're gonna have these students that are for it. Especially with all the experiences they've had. And the regular thought is, "this is the way it goes." I say to my students, sometimes I say, "you do not have to simplify. I actually don't want you to. I want to see it messy. But I also understand that it is a preference of mine. And some of you are very uncomfortable about simplifying. And if that is your case, go ahead. I may have to mark you off, if you simplify incorrectly, because I have to point out to you an error so that you know where it is. But I will always look at the answer pre-simplified. Engage in that answer. And if it's a simplification, I will point it out to you to be careful. "Yeah, here you're multiplying by a negative and you dropped the negative." Just because it works for me, doesn't mean it's going to work for everyone. And that is the thing with radical grace. I have to remember. They are whole people who had whole lives before they came in. They don't just appear with me in that space, when I walk in, ready to do whatever I say. And I want to honor that, with hearing their voices of what they're thinking about in the classroom. With seeing them do things, I want to create a space where they can show me who they are, mathematically or with English, or the language that they speak, or the way they see things, or things they've never heard of, and I get to explain it to them or thoughts on random things. Like I want them to feel like this space is our space. And

I tell students all the time, they're like, "oh, everyone loves your class." And I was like, "no, not everyone loves my class. It's propaganda. It's propaganda. There are people who don't like it. And that is fine. I'm not for everyone. And that's okay." Nobody's for everyone. There are people who don't like Beyoncé music. I know some people in my family that don't. Everyone is not for everyone. That's okay. Everyone gets to be whole people.

M: There are always counterexamples in life, always counterexamples.

C: There are always counterexamples, and there are always outliers. Yeah, and those are two different things.

M: What do you mean?

C: So a counterexample means that this thing is not always true as a whole. So I think sometimes we look at one thing, and we're like, well, the whole system is broken. That didn't work for this one situation, I'm gonna throw it away. And I think we often think about that with changing how things work in spaces, no matter all the other data we have. And so that's why I think sometimes we have outliers. All the other data we have is doing really well. And this one student was like, "screw active learning. I am not interested." And that's not a counterexample to active learning. Because a counterexample would mean, "active learning doesn't work in my class, because not everyone thought it was great. So I need to drop it." But the outlier is telling you information about the data. It's telling you information about what you're doing. And you think, okay, how do I adjust this information? What is the outlier in this case? Versus "Oh, this is a counter example. I have to drop this idea." And so yes, there are counterexamples to the "everyone loves you." And then there are outliers, which is telling me, "what is it that I need to adjust?"

What does education look like when radical grace is the norm? We don't know exactly, but it has to look different than what we have today. We believe it will more inclusive. It will include restoration. It will be spaces that are co-created by instructor and student. Spaces where everyone is provided and providing grace. It is a re-humanizing of educational spaces... and it is not impossible.

Appendix A

Appendix A: RAMP UP Seminar

THIS WAS A TALK GIVEN VIRTUALLY at the University of Oklahoma Mathematics Department. RAMP UP means: Resources in Alternative Methods of Pedagogy for University Professionals. Talks range from learning about new or changing teaching technologies, brainstorming sessions on trying different techniques, disseminating data about how trying a new technique went, book club meetings, and has served as a pandemic teaching support group.

We were invited and had a chat similar to our podcast and this book. It had many of the similar ideas, themes, and even metaphors that we've used before, with some new ideas sprinkled in. We had a great discussion with a few participants asking questions and sharing their own experiences or difficulties of radical grace in the classroom.

M: You ready, Candice? All right.

C: Okay. Oh, because you wanted to do the intro? Yes. Oh my gosh, sorry. This is the intro of the podcast that we are creating, hence the recording, and so: radical, far reaching or thorough.

M: Grace, courteous goodwill.

Both: Radical grace.

C: You're wrong every time. He waits to hear me before he talks right. And so he's behind because every time.

M: I just want to say I'm extremely thankful for Candice's grace, in providing me grace to screw up every single time on the intro. Candice, I have got a just a tiny question for you. What is your definition of radical grace?

C: Yeah. So, one of the things that I try to think about is when I'm interacting with my students, there is always a sort of a power dynamic that is happening, that they look at me, and they think that I have all the power in that situation, and that we are at odds with each other. In some way, there's this animosity that we have. They have to prove to me that they are worthy of a grade that they are getting, that I'm giving them, in fact, and that's often the conversation: "well, you *gave* me this grade."

One of the things I think about with radical grace is it's not just a pedagogy. It's not a set of rules of things that should happen. It's more of a space that I'm creating in my classroom, that allows for each of us to see one another as teammates as partners, and allows for us to ask for the support that we need. Each of us, right? I'm in that space as well as a full human. And there are some days where I need my students to be patient with me because I'm tired, or I've had just like a bad night or not, or I'm just not fully prepared. And instead of feeling, going into that space and feeling bad about being a human, we're all allowed to bring our full selves into that space. And so for me, that's what radical grace means. It's how I'm interacting with the students in a way that allows all of us to bring our full selves into it. What about you, Miloš?

M: I mean, it's the radical part that I think kind of hits me every single time we've talked about it, because I think grace happens every once in a while. It's the part "far reaching," right? It's going a little bit extra or pushing some of the norms or bounds that have already been set up or that are preordained from history. I think a lot about when I went through school, and the stuff that occurred in my life, or has been occurring. I think about how, instead of worrying about having to get every single homework done on every single time, when I'm doing it like 25% because I'm just trying to get it done for that day. Right? If I could have had a moment where a professor came to the side and was just like, "look, I don't know what's happening. Take your time. Because you're not going to understand it or be able to absorb it fully if you don't have all of those working memory chunks available to you."

You said it – there's animosity, right. But that's a preconceived notion that goes on in the classroom, not post-conceived. People come in with this notion that, "okay, the teacher is going to be a person that's going to fight me," or they're going to be very harsh or this or that. And it's not even limited to what goes on – there is an undercurrent. My girls are reading a book, where the teacher is like, mean. Like, there are certain things that are kind of pre-conceiving all of this, right?

I always think about what instances, what times, and what moments I could have received grace in certain areas. It's radical because of the fact that there seems to be this like, norm that there shouldn't be grace. And I think that's the hardest thing for me to kind of even unlearn myself. You know, I'm still going through this. What has gone on in your background or in your academic career that has led you towards radical grace?

C: I mean, excellent question. Excellent segue, sir. I think we've had similar things happen, right, where we're undergraduates, and some-thing's happening in our lives. So I'll say for myself instead of we state-ments, but when I was an undergrad, first-gen, I didn't know what I was doing all the time. I was working a job because I thought I needed extra money. I did need extra money for I don't know what I was spending it on. I wish I had that money now. And I was working this job at six in the morning. And then I had a 9am class. So I would go from my six-in-the-morning job to my 9am class. And I also lived in this house with like eight other girls that would like party every night. And I'm like, "Well, I have to go to bed at this time. Because I have to be up at five to be at my six-in-the-morning job." And I would sleep through that class. I would go to the class and I would sleep. And my instructor never talked to me. Never asked like, "what's going on? Are you doing okay?" And I always felt like it was assumed that I just didn't care. Because this is, I think, one of the things we're conditioned to believe about our students is that if they care, they will look like this, right? They'll be attentive, they'll sit in the front, they'll take notes, right? They'll be this ideal student. And while I wanted to be there, obviously I was there in class, I just couldn't stay awake, because I was so tired. And so there wasn't this opportunity, I think, where my instructor reached out to me and just said, "I've noticed this, what can I do to support you?" And for me, that's grace. But apparently, that's radical, because already in their mind they have this other idea, and I'm speculating based on them not talking to me.

And I think that that's the issue we have right, the animosity based on them not speaking to me, I assumed they didn't care. And so when I decided that this is the profession I wanted to go into, education, and I wanted to be a professor, so one of the things I thought about was how can I change the relationship my students have with me that I didn't have with my instructors. Unless you're saying, "I'm learning this every day, every semester," there's an adaptation. Every semester I meet with my students, I reflect on how that went. And I think about what things can I adjust. And also I come into the space with my new students, like they may need something different than my previous class. Let me be open to the fact that I do not have this fixed mindset about interacting with students.

It's more of an equity issue versus equality. What did they need in this moment? Not what do students need but what are *these* students needing? What does this individual need this moment? And I think that's what makes it [radical grace]. Also, because I think we're trained, at least I should say, stop saying we statements, but I was trained to come into the classroom and be so hard right away, super tough, because they will take advantage of you. And then you can lessen in the end, right? You have to be very rigid. And then once in a while, you can give some pushback.

And I used to do that. And what I realized was that I was assuming my students didn't deserve support until they proved to me, they deserve support. So already, we're coming in and clashing. And then at some moment, I get to decide, "oh, okay, you have put enough tokens into the machine. And now I can give you grace." Instead of just coming in, and providing that for them, or showing them that at the beginning, right, so that we can have that back and forth relationship where they understand if I need something. And I'm not asking them like, "write me a doctor's note, or I need an essay to tell me why you need these things." Right? If they need something, that I can provide, then I'll do it. So they're not afraid to ask. I couldn't ask for more time in the class that I was sleeping, and I was too afraid. This person is gonna think I'm such a bum without understanding that I'm working, and I'm living in this situation. And it's not the best for a student, but this is what I have. And can we work around? Can I find some support? And what's happening with me? So I think, all of that I have in the back of my mind when I walk into the classroom on the first day, and every day after that, I'm thinking, "how am I interacting with my students in a way that they feel support? And they feel like they can do well, and that we are in this together and not afraid? To talk to me?"

M: Yeah, it's the same fear that doesn't allow for, or it's the same fear and worry about question-asking [in class]. It's the same fear and worry about meeting in groups and talking with one another and being afraid to expose what you don't know, or what you need help on.

It's interesting to me about talking about grace. I start every semester now, and to be honest with you all, I think the pandemic has pushed me into radical grace, exponentially. So now the bulk of the first day, it's like, "Please, look, let me know what's going on. Or don't let me know, just say, hey, I need something, right. And then, and then we go from there." But that's *all talk*. I believe that radical grace is not just saying, "Hey, I'm gonna give you grace," because that can be great and all, but then your actions afterwards are not showing grace. I'm trying myself every semester to sit down and go, "Okay, did my actions in my classroom align with what I'm believing in?" And I really appreciate you telling us about what happened working, going to class, et cetera, et cetera. That was then [for Candice], I don't know what students are going through in 2022. I really don't. I'm sorry. We went through 56k modems. Now you have the internet at your fingertips.

C: Right. I just want to say it's very interesting because I walk into the classroom. Sometimes things happen on campus, and you have a conversation with your class about it. And I said,

"Listen, I don't actually know how to have this conversation with you. Because I don't know the lives you're living. I don't. I live a very different life than you right now. And I lived a different life than you. When I was an undergrad. There's so many things that are different, but what I do know is that you're a whole person living outside of this space, and you deserve the support. It's not something you have to earn. We all deserve this support this grace. And so what I can give you is this, this moment in time when we're talking about mathematics. And if that's not what you need at this time, I hope that you know, I can help you find something different or lead you to the people who can do something different."

And I think that's spot on, Miloš, we don't know. And we shouldn't have to know in order to care about our students. I don't want my students to tell me every detail about their lives. I always thought it was so weird that people would ask for [permission], and no offense to anyone that does this. And I don't want it to be a judgment call at all. I'm just saying, it's weird to me. When people ask for notes from doctors, or the funeral pamphlets, if they have to go to a funeral, I'm like, "what do you do with that? You put that in a file somewhere? And you just have this file?" What if we could just say, "Okay, no problem, you need this time, you need a bit more space?" Like, what if we just believed our students? I mean, because I don't need to know your full life to know that you're human. And you're asking for something. And it's something I can provide. So why don't I provide it?

I also want to say that I know we're talking a lot about radical grace looking like giving someone extra time to do something or space. But I think it's also an understanding that if you're giving, if there's too much rope, or too much time, the impact that has on a student, that is also radical grace. Because you're actually not helping a student if they have to kick the can all the way down to the last month, and they have like 100 assignments to do last month, you're not actually helping them in that situation. You're not supporting them, you're actually giving, you know, my mom used to say, too much rope. So also understanding and having those conversations that are difficult, like, "but if we move this assignment, let's see what our schedule looks like, and how that will impact you down the line. Okay, are we setting ourselves up for success? Or for failure in this situation? Right? What other things can we do that might help a little bit more?" So I just want to make sure that we aren't saying like, "well, there are no deadlines and do whatever you want," because that actually isn't grace. That's not the kind of grace we're talking. There still has to be some structure and there has to be support, grace with support. It's like, what is the metaphor we use? I think it's the parachute metaphor. We think about it as we're pulling or pushing someone out of a plane, but we're giving them a parachute. So there's two ways to do this. You can push someone out of a plane without the parachute like, "well, good luck, learn to fly." Or you could like strap them on to you and jump out of the parachute out of the plane with them. And they'd be like, "see, do you see how easy this is?" Neither one of those actually helps them learn how to do the things you do. So you have to give support and grace. You have to give all of those things in one situation.

M: I think so. I always think of the trampoline, or some kind of net underneath. I could do the puzzle for you, or I could never do [anything with] your puzzle for hours and hours. with both of those, I don't know if there's support I'm providing right. I also want to say when you're pulling up the math 100 app, default settings should be set to radical grace. I think about this: what are the default settings of the classroom? Are you accepting all cookies? It's amazing to me. It's amazing to me how hard it is to break norms. There is going to be conflict; there is going to be a fight. There are some students for which after 16 weeks, they won't believe that you're gonna give them grace still. But that's okay. I mean, this is a very hard thing.

It took me years to kind of unlearn some of the aspects that go on. I don't want to say this is like a checklist thing. As you said before, it's a belief. No matter what scenario – if you have eight or you have 8000 students. If you believe in radical grace, sure, it's going to look a little bit different in these different ways, because [of the different] scenarios, but that belief, coupled with the actions, [radical grace is] going to show. I always think about this, like before, and I still have huge anxiety when the email comes up about your evaluations. Because I'm always so scared that I did everything wrong or I'm gonna get fired. Literally every semester before tenure, I thought that I was gonna get fired after those evals. It's true. I think about this now, if I'm in a mindset of radical grace, and I am co-creating, I should never say creating, because I'm only one person in this deal. There's 40 others that are in the deal, right? If I'm trying the best I can to give as much as I can to help my students succeed, then I can lay down every night feeling like I tried. And that's a big, big deal.

That's a huge shift from going, "well, you didn't do this, or you didn't do that" [Now it's like,] "Okay, I tried my best, and I'm gonna learn from this experience." And that's not to say that I don't see the evals. I look through them, and I go, "Oh, yes, that's something I need to do." I'll always remember a spring 2019 eval, where the person said, "he values mistakes in class, but he never values them on the test." Oh, excuse me. I'm not being consistent with my values. So the next semester, I wrote a five point question that said, "can you tell me the worst mistake or the worst way you could approach this problem? What's the biggest mistake you can make on this problem?" One student said, "to not try." And I almost started tearing up on that one. But, even then, there's grace right there. I think now it's me thinking about like, "what are my actions doing? And are they aligning towards this belief that radical grace is needed in the classroom," It's switching from like, "this student missed class, so they don't like me, or they don't like the class" or anything else, all this negativity, to more of like, "How can I figure out ways to help them?" At least I'm not, I'm not a counselor, I'm not a health professional. So how can I guide them to professionals that can help them on their journey? Because, honestly, whether it was me not having radical grace, or me having radical grace, I still wanted my students to succeed. It was just the mindset of like, success is through me. Being strict like you said and then giving a little. Now, success is me just trying to foster the the incredible thoughts and ideas that they already have.

And I always feel like that grace is a beautiful spiral forward. I can tell in even interactions in group time that some students are giving other students radical grace within the group. That they're approaching them instead of being frustrated or mad. They're trying to figure out what's going on. That's huge. That's a big deal.

M: We have some extra stuff on our questions here. But do you all have any questions for us?

C: Yeah, we've been talking a bit which we can keep going.

Attendee 1: I have a question. So part of what you were saying was talking about the idea of you making a decision that radical grace is necessary or something that is important to you, or one of your values. And I know, you've addressed a handful of things like the situation changes, or maybe radical grace looks something like this for this student, and this for another student, it looks like this on this day, it looks like this on this other day. I guess when you have a group of people who feel similarly to you, that you can like talk with or bounce ideas off of to work through those things. That seems like a really nice thing. What about those times when you don't? What about those times when you're in a situation where you might say, I'm going to enact radical grace like this, but maybe there's policy, maybe you're collaborating with someone, maybe something else? How do you overcome those kinds of things, as you're transforming your thinking?

C: Yeah, I think this is a really, really great question. I think a lot of times people say, Yeah, but you did this in your class, and then we go to another class. And [radical grace is] not going to happen, and they're not prepared for that. And so I think one of the things that makes it radical is we are fighting against this norm system, it's sort of like you're walking the opposite direction on one of those, like moving walkways, and everybody else is being carried on the moving walkway, but you're trying to go the opposite direction. And it's very tiring and stressful. And I have experienced this because I teach a calculus class that is coordinated. So there are specific things. So the way that radical grace looks different is in the kinds of conversations I'm having with the students in that space, and the kinds of things I can control and give them more time on but I also let them know. "So this is a sort of structured thing that this class has. Okay. And so how can I support you to to be able to do this structured thing and the way that you need to for this course." It's difficult though, because it is hard to to not be able to just be like whatever we want to do, or we can do. Because we rarely get that opportunity. Gosh, it feels so good when we do, but we're still living in this space that the norm is maybe something that isn't radical grace, and which makes it *radical*.

We all are very idealistic, Miloš and I, we hold that at one point [hopefully] radical grace is no longer radical, it's just the norm in our classroom spaces. But coming into the class and letting them know, "I am here to support you in ways that you need, I am seeing you as a whole person." I think that's the baseline for radical grace. And that fits in every kind of class. And then there is some maneuvering that needs to happen, depending on the structure of that course. Of course, I think a lot of people ask us, "Well, how do I do this if it's a 200-person class? I can't give everyone all the time. And it's like, "it may be true, but you could also just move the deadline for everyone." There are different things that can happen. But different things that you can't do. Like, I can't meet with every single student for 30 minutes if I have a 200 person class. That's impossible. But what can I do? Can I meet with groups? Can I email each of them once a week? And just be like, "how's it going? Just checking in." What are the things that we can do? So a lot of this does have to be adapted, depending on the situation that you're in. But I think the, the foundation has to be, "I'm here to support my students, and I'm seeing them as a whole person."

Attendee 2: Can I jump in here, maybe? So what you were just touching on, it's something you touched on earlier, is the cost of radical grace for the instructor because this is something that I'm really focused on. Because for me, the cost is high, too. And I'm just going to talk about my situation for a second, I get the emails saying I have this situation, every assignment, every single assignment, so you just had a suggestion of like, move it back for everybody. I'm moving my whole schedule. I think I'm, especially in this conversation. I'm pretty happy with the policy I do have, because I do view it as [radical grace]. I don't know. I'm pretty content with what I have set up. But I guess what I would love to hear y'all talk about is the the cost of radical grace, but then also kind of a perspective of suggestions for having the students view your radical grace as being radical grace, because sometimes the students view my policy of "we're going to drop so many low scores," and all is forgiven. "If you can't do this assignment, don't do it. That's okay. You know, you can get caught up later on your time. But it's like not going to hurt your grade." And it's a battle still trying to get the students to understand that is my radical grace. If they view it as a grade booster, then they don't view it as radical grace. And for me, it's not a grade booster, it's a forgiveness amount. I guess I'd love to hear y'all talk about the students like trying to have those conversations in helping students see your radical grace.

M: I'm just going to say quickly, I think one thing that I keep thinking about, and it's kind of like active learning if you believe in it, it may look different to everybody else. We have talked about this many of times – mimicking may not work. I think that's the same with radical grace. Like, we're saying stuff, Candice and I, but it could mean totally different things to you, as long as the belief is there, that you do want to provide grace. Again, I've had a hard time, unlearning reciprocation. If I do this, then you're going to do this back. If I give grace then they're going to give grace back. Well, that's not guaranteed. No action from some other person other than myself is guaranteed. And so I think about that a lot. When I think about in the classroom, I can provide this grace, and they may not provide or write it back to me. They may never provide it back.

Attendee 1: I heard that put in a really interesting way recently. It's not a gift if you expect something in return.

M: Yeah. And so I think that's a big deal. I always think about pre-empting things. This happened in the classroom for this classroom. What can I do the next semester, so that I can preempt what may happen in the future? The first thing that came to my mind was like being open and honest about the grading policies, and why I believe that they're providing grace. That may be one step. Now, it's not a guarantee at all. But let's try that for next semester, or write up a little bit in the syllabus. The more I've been explicit with students, the more at least they get to know where I'm coming from. And one last thing, we talked about this actually a couple of days ago, seeing your students as whole people, that may also be reciprocated, as well, because they see you in the grocery store. And they're like, "oh, my gosh, Dr. Savić loves avocados. I couldn't believe that – all I thought is that he reads RUME papers. 24/7." So I think that that's kind of the big deal here is that it's incredible what radical grace can provide. Giving radical grace, you don't know. But you know, that you're trying to provide as positive, as uplifting, as supportive an atmosphere as you can.

C: I just also want to say thank you to Attendee 2 for this question, because I think we have been talking about it without talking about the cost that it has on us as faculty members. And it's true. I mean, you're right. I said like, "Oh, could you move all of it?" And you're like, "No," and that's okay. It's okay to say no to that, and how that impacts you. Because you also deserve radical grace. You also have to think about how is this impacting me? I am never asking anyone to carve themselves up to give away to their students. I have this joke, like I do so much, but I'm not like gonna give my kidney. We're not saying like, to your detriment, do everything possible for them at all? And really, it would be hard to say no, I know. And I really appreciate you saying, but what about the effort and the time it puts on us? And you're absolutely correct.

That's why [radical grace] has to look different. Because I can't say, "Well, I do this in my class." And you don't say you're not providing radical grace. Like that's not what this is at all. And it's true, I think, you said every time someone asks you, and I think I would agree with Miloš, which says is, every semester, my first day, setting the stage [activity] gets longer and longer, because there's more things I have learned to say to them, more sort of transparency. "We drop this many things because it's a full week of material. So for one full week, you could just be like, I can't do any of this. And it's okay, because it all gets dropped no matter what. You don't have to ask for that. It's just dropped because it's zero in the book. And if you need more than that, then we should have a conversation. Because something else is going on. And let's have that conversation." And so I say that to them first day, right? And reiterate when they ask like "oh, can I have more time?" I'm like, "Well, while we dropped this because [of something], pushing it down the line means this." I am having those kinds of conversations with them over email or in person.

But I totally get it that this does take work, because we're working against against this sort of norm. And I think often, when students ask me for more and more time on something like same student, maybe, then I have to pull them aside like, "what's going on? Because I think me giving you this more time isn't actually helping you as much as I think it is, or as much as you think it is. What do you really need?" And sometimes that's a conversation I just have with them. Sometimes it's a conversation I'm having with their advisor, sometimes it's a conversation I'm having with them. Let's actually find a way to help you because I cannot put a BandAid on a knife wound. So yeah, I just thank you. Thank you for asking that, because I think that is a very good question.

M: But it's you not coming in with judgment about what they think about the knife wound. Right? It's you coming in going, "Hey, I don't know. But what can I do to help?" I think that's different from what we described earlier on, which is assuming that we knew, assuming that this is what's going on. And then that's it. And I think that's a huge turning point in my life, where I was like, "Look, instead of making all these assumptions that I'm making about students, why don't I just ask them? Or even why don't I just engage in a conversation where they feel a little bit more comfortable?" To even just say, "hey, look, I need time." It's a big deal to me.

C: Can I also say that sometimes students fall through the cracks. I'm gonna say that now, just so that it doesn't seem like I have this cape, and [you think] I'm just doing this perfectly. Because perfectionism is a characteristic of white supremacy culture, and I'm not perfect. If I tried to do that, then that's what I'm upholding. And so I will say that happens. So for me, when I first think about grace, I think about forgiveness. And there are moments where I'm not going to be the best, whatever that is, that I can be. I have to be able to forgive the fact that I didn't do that. And this semester has been very hard. I know that I'm not doing all the things that I couldn't be doing, and that I have to just be okay with that, because I'm giving myself grace and forgiveness in that time. Sometimes we have to, we have to also do that. Put the mask on yourself first when the plane's going down before you can help others. There are moments where we have to make that decision.

M: What a metaphor. Yes. It was exactly the question I was going to ask you is, do you provide yourself any radical grace? I mean, that was the question that was asked in the room. I talked about this talk yesterday. And one of the students asked if I provided myself, or how do I even provide myself especially when I have screwed up so many times in my teaching in the past. I actually said something that I had never said before. I said something to the effect of like, "what if I don't give myself radical grace, then what's going to happen?"

I don't know. I think it would be difficult. And so it's reflection, it's knowing that I can try to be better. It's knowing that I can make mistakes. And it's knowing that, you said students fall through the cracks. There are days where I fall through the cracks. I think that's actually a huge thing. Can I say we all fall? I think everybody, everybody else has obstacles. I always think about this when I did my research on incubation. If we didn't have like sticking points, we'd have all the math created. Every person in life has a sticking point in mathematics. And I'm sure it happens in life. One of the biggest aspects of my life has been how I've gotten up because I've fell so many times. It's how I pick myself back up that's made me who I am. That involves like giving myself grace a little bit to pick myself back up.

Attendee 1: I just want to know. I think part of the conversation is the things I was saying earlier, it's really nice to have a group of people. I spent a lot of time having really great conversations with other people in the department. But I think we get to the place where we're safe to have those conversations, because we have already sort of set up this network of trust. And so when you try something out, you kind of understand everybody's motivations. I don't have to like, I don't have to, like write a thesis explaining to Miloš, why I feel the way that I feel about something. You know, because we share so many values in that way. I think part of the issue that I run into, is kind of the flip side of Attendee 2's question. So her question was, you know, how do you consider the cost to the instructor? Since my daughter was very small, the analogy of put your mask on first has been something that I've always kind of thought about when I'm making those decisions.

The bump up that I run into is kind of the opposite way when somebody else is telling me I don't think I want to pay that kind of cost. I don't think you should either. Or having to talk to people about defending why I'm doing what I'm doing. Sometimes the conversation with an advisor, with a student, or with a department chair or Dean or something, is not "how can we help the student," but, "why did you help these students so much?" Or "why is your policy like this?" That's the labyrinth that I'm kind of sort of learning. I'm still in the phase where I'm trying to figure out, "how much rope is too much rope?" But talking to other people who haven't kind of started coming to this transition of viewing the student as a whole individual, like what can you say [to them]?

C: Yes, I have also gotten this advice about sort of like "you're doing too much for the students" or something like that. I worry. When someone says to me that they're trying to take away my advocacy, like, "I can't make choices for myself," like, "oh, we have to help her, she doesn't understand how this works." And so one of the things that I tried to do is show the outcome. "Yeah, you're right, I did spend a lot of time with that student. But here's the outcome of that. This student now feels differently about mathematics or not. But this is what we saw happen. And this is what we now understand about the students situation, and how in the future, what positive, forward momentum they'll have, because of the time that I spent with them or not." And then I'm like, "Yeah, you know, I learned a lot about my interaction with that student, I learned how much rope. But if I think about all of these interactions as reflections on ways that I want to be better, or I want a better instructor, or I want my students to have better experiences, then that is what I will share with people about what that time means." Because I think a lot of people think about time as numbers. And time is money, versus time as experiences and just feelings for the student.

And for myself, what have I learned in that time? Sure, I could watch a two hour lecture on YouTube and not understand anything, or I could spend two hours reading. It's the same amount of time, but what did I get out of it? That's kind of how I've been doing that when that comes up for me. So that's like, "oh, you spent $100 on this bookshelf?" "Yeah, but this is what this bookshelf does." I don't know – that metaphor was weird. You show the value of that time. I think explaining to them and, and even saying, "ask the student what they learned from their time with me?" Because that's what we're doing here. I don't understand it. That's what we're doing here.

M: No, that's exactly what I was gonna say. I would ask back, "what's the goal of all of this? What is our collective end game here? Is it that students learn? Well, then, I'm trying my best, in my way, to help students learn." I used to always think that active learning is so important. And I've got paper A and paper B and paper C [that can prove that active learning is important]. Why does the default have to be lecture, and I've got to prove that active learning is good over and over again? What if the default was radical grace or grace, period? "Now prove to me why you have to be so hard on people."

Attendee 1: I think that's kind of coming up to my experiences. Like sometimes the issue is that somebody has a lot of data points that they believe or support, "This is why grace is not beneficial." So for example, a conversation that I've had with students this semester, so for the pandemic, things have just... I've tried to apply the same grace to the students that I hope people are applying to me because I have felt like I'm holding on by my fingernails. I can't remember when I started doing it, but that there are hard deadlines and soft deadlines. So there's this idea that, "okay, if you're doing this in the ideal way, this is when you will do learn this information. And hey, if you do, I might even give you feedback so that you can learn from it and then resubmit. No big deal. Maybe you're having terrible things happen. Maybe you're sick, maybe you're working extra, maybe you're taking care of someone. So it's fine. If you didn't do it this week, just get it into me by the end of the semester." Making it very clear that this is why I'm doing it.

And the number of students this semester who have talked to me about how well all of my other instructors have only hard deadlines, so your stuff has been pushed to the side, because we just had midterms. So, I was taking some students aside, pointing at the Gradebook. What a lot of them said was, "Your deadlines are not hard deadlines. And so I haven't really been prioritizing your stuff. I know that I should." And so, that's part of what they're learning is time management. It's on the horizon. But I guess the part that I'm seeing, though, is that at the end of this, that student's going to learn about time management, that students going to learn about prioritizing. That student doesn't have to pass the course to be successful. Yes, they made progress. If they made a life altering discovery about themselves, their boundaries, their limits, that's not going to show up on their transcript. But now somebody's going to have a data point that says, "Look, you gave so much grace, but that person never got their assignments finished, and they failed."

M: It's such a short-term thinking though. "I'm gonna, I'm gonna look at just what happened in 16 weeks. And that's it." I've had a student come up to me in the middle of dinner, I was at a dinner, and they came up to me and they were just like, "Dr. Savić, I failed your course. I learned so much about how to handle things and how to overcome things from that." Like, it's something that we didn't press on a bunch. But radical grace is not about like, "Oh, we're going to have like, one plus two, on every exam," right? It is also coupled with challenge and actually pretty difficult challenge too. It's what keeps coming up in the equity literature when it comes to like, fostering STEM equity. It's about challenge, but also care. And we can do both. I think that this whole binary-ness of everything frustrates me quite a bit.

Another thing that frustrates me kind of quite a bit is the zero-sum game of what goes on in a classroom. If I do this, I don't do this. And I understand time is a zero-sum game. But there are other actions that if you provide one, many will benefit from. I loved you inviting the ADRC (Accessibility and Disability Resource Center) person to come to RAMP UP. And she talked about when you have math text, that there should be a providing of what that math text means. And not only is that going to be helpful for those that are diagnosed with disabilities, but also it's going to help others trying to understand what's going on with the math. It's a perfect example of that it's not a zero-sum game, that I'm not only helping a group of students but helping many with this. You can feel the environment in week 10, week 11, where students are giving grace to others, or they're supporting others, or they're fighting for others. When that happens, many people are winning in that scenario, and so, to me, I get frustrated by this. I understand where you're coming from with all this because you're trying to justify something that there's no numbers for. There's no letters. It is much bigger than that.

C: Just vibes.

Attendee 1: I think a lot of it is.. It depends on the metric that somebody is using. [How do you] measure what is success? What is help? I think the issue that I'm running into is, right now I'm in a mind space from the last two years of like, "listen, it's okay to get a C as long as you lived through the semester. Like, did you sleep? Did you eat? Did you drink? Oh, that means you got a C. Oh, well."

Attendee 3: I think something that we hear a lot when when it's like arguing against grace, is saying, "well, in the real world, they don't get to turn in their late work. There's not a makeup test in the real world. But think about the last time that we needed a late due date. And we took it, it was every day. So we, it's every day all the time. And last I checked, I think I am living in the real world. Yeah, people in the real world working jobs, always take a late due date.

Attendee 1: It's even bigger than that, though. Like, think about this, we can talk about the idea of whether or not we agree with them or not, or whether or not they're equitable. But there are systems in place where that does happen in the real world. If you make a mistake, with your bank account, you get grace, they don't like throw you in prison, they just charge you a fee. If you are not on time paying back your loan, they don't imprison you, or send out the firing squad, they charge you interest. Like there's late due dates all the time. That's what they mean, just in the financial market. That happens constantly. I mean, we can talk about whether or not that's equitable, because it's not. But that's just a problem with that system. It just exists though, those kinds of things happen. The policy of taking your child to daycare, if you don't pick them up at six o'clock, then you're getting charged $5 every minute that you're late or whatever. Like, that's grace to they're not going to throw your kid out on the street, they'll just charge you for it.

M: But how can we get it to the radical part? How can we do it to where the daycare is like, "Hey, is everything okay? Are you all okay? Like, do we need, you know, I don't know, we can help you as much as we can help you." How does it become a society that starts going, "Hey, look, you've been late three times? Is everything okay?" Instead of like, "you've been late three times, I'm going to charge you $25 each time and et cetera, et cetera." I think this is a first step to me of many other steps that need to be kind of absorbed, much like talking about mathematics and how mathematics is perceived in the world and everything else. These are all first steps that I'm trying to take. But can we take it together? Can we support each other in that whole thing? I think that's a big, big deal. Because yes, you're right there. There are people who don't believe in what we're saying at all. That there is one way and it's their way.

Attendee 1: What we've discovered a lot during this last handful of years seeing the way that our systems either do or don't fall apart under some sort of notable event. There are things that have happened that you know, before it was "oh my gosh, it's just doesn't happen, the world will collapse." And it turns out that it was fine. You know, and then other things that were so tenuous, that when people had to stay home for two weeks, suddenly we realize like, "oh, no, that that was shaky." But I think, based on that same thing, though, that's where I think Attendee 2's question about cost comes in, when you feel like you are refreshed when you feel like you have your oxygen mask on first, when you feel like you don't have to be giving yourself grace, you have more grace to give. But when somebody says, "Man, I would really love to talk to you about why you've been late three times, is there something I can do to help you," when you feel like you're hanging on by a thread? You don't have the grace to give that person. And I think that's the balance of running into like, it's really awesome when I have like a cohort, a community of people who support me. But since we don't live off the grid in a commune.

C: Yet. Growth mindset here. Yet.

M: Can I add by saying that a community of people to talk to and that give me grace, or that belief in me, to allow me to think that I actually *deserve* to have a mask on in the airplane? Because by myself, I don't think I would have felt that way, or through society or through growing up. I don't know if I would have felt that way. So to me, I think that's one of the many benefits of having community that supports, that gives grace to each other, that wants to help and build, is that when that oxygen mask comes down, I'd be like, "Well, no, I don't deserve."

Attendee 1: There's these new little round of BetterHelp commercials, those like online counseling sort of things are very funny. So like, I've seen, I've seen a handful of them. One of them is a, a cowboy out on the range, like they're driving their cattle or whatever. And he's been bitten by a rattlesnake. So he's like, carrying all his stuff. And he's like, stumbling. And his, his partner is like, "Hey, do you need some help? Are you okay? We should work, we should help you out." And he's like, "No, I'll be fine. My daddy told me that, you know, so like the idea of, I'm not going to admit that I'm having trouble." Or there's another one where a guy is like, he's in the gym, and he's lifted something. And he refuses to accept the spotters help. Because he's like, "What if my parents and my family find out that I'm struggling with it? I could never."

M: Yeah, and normalizing accepting all of this stuff.? One of my biggest drivers of believing in radical grace is my family, my kids and [saying to myself], "how am I acting towards a better future for them?" Not saying, not talking, but how am I acting towards that? And part of that has to be the radical grace part. Candice, thank you.

C: You're welcome! Thank you.

Appendix B

Appendix B: References, Resources, and Inspiration

- Anything by Aditya Adiredja, including: Adiredja, A. P. (2019). Anti-deficit narratives: Engaging the politics of research on mathematical sense making. *Journal for Research in Mathematics Education, 50*(4), 401-435.

- Todos Cuentan: Cultivating Diversity in Combinatorics, by Federico Ardila-Mantilla

- Anything by Erika Bullock, including: Bullock, E. C. (2013). Conducting "good" equity research in mathematics education: A question of methodology. *Journal of Mathematics Education at Teachers College, 3*(2).

- Creativity Research Group (www.creativityresearchgroup.com)

- Pedagogy of the Oppressed, by Paulo Freire

- Anything by Rochelle Gutiérrez, including: Gutiérrez, R. (2018). Introduction: The Need to Rehumanize Mathematics. In I. Goffney, R. Gutiérrez, & M. Boston (Eds.), *Rehumanizing Mathematics for Black, Indigenous, and Latinx Students (Annual Perspectives in Mathematics Education; Vol. 2018)*. National Council of Teachers of Mathematics.

- Teaching to Transgress, by bell hooks – the whole book is fire.

- Anything by Estrella Johnson, including: Johnson, E., Andrews-Larson, C., Keene, K., Keller, R., Fortune, N., & Melhuish, K. (2020). Inquiry and inequity in the undergraduate mathematics classroom. *Journal for Research in Mathematics Education. 51*(4), 504-516.

- Anything by Gregory Larnell, including: Larnell, G. V. (2016). More than just skill: Examining mathematics identities, racialized narratives, and remediation among black undergraduates. *Journal for Research in Mathematics Education, 47*(3), 233-269.

- Anything by Luis Leyva, including: Leyva, L. A., Quea, R., Weber, K., Battey, D., & López, D. (2021). Detailing racialized and gendered mechanisms of undergraduate precalculus and calculus classroom instruction. *Cognition and Instruction, 39*(1), 1-34.

- The Value of Struggle, by Francis Su

- The Lesson of Grace in Teaching, by Francis Su

- Conversations and Twitter posts from an incredible amount of people in our lives.